Engineering the future

ELECTRICIAN'S GUIDE TO THE BUILDING REGULATIONS

Including Approved Document P:
Electrical Safety in Dwellings

(Applicable in England and Wales – SI 2531 – 2000)

Published by: The IEE, LONDON, UK

The IEE
P.O. Box 96
Stevenage
SG1 2SD, UK
Tel: +44 (0)1438 767 328
Email: sales@iee.org
http://www.iee.org/Publish/Books/WireAssoc/

ISBN 0 86341 463 X

Contents

Co-operating Organisations

The IEE acknowledges the contribution made by the following organisations in the preparation of this Guide:

Association of Manufacturers of Domestic Electrical Appliances
S A MacConnacher BSc CEng MIEE M Inst R

BEAMA Ltd
R F B Lewington MIEE and
P D Galbraith I Eng MIIE MIEE MCMI

BEAMA Installations Ltd
Eur Ing M H Mullins BA CEng FIEE FIIE and
P Sayer IEng MIIE GCGI

British Cables Association
C K Reed I Eng MIIE

British Standards Institution
D Wade

City & Guilds of London Institute
H R Lovegrove IEng FIIE

Electrical Contractors' Association
D Locke IEng MIIE ACIBSE and
G Digilio

Electrical Contractors' Association of Scotland (SELECT)
D Millar IEng MIIE MILE

Electricity Networks Association Limited
D J Start BSc CEng MIEE

EMTA Awards Ltd

ERA Technology Ltd
M W Coates BEng

Federation of the Electronics Industry
F W Pearson CEng MIIE

The GAMBICA Association Ltd
K A Morriss BSc CEng MIEE

Institution of Electrical Engineers
J Ware BSc CEng MIEE
G G Willard DipEE CEng MIEE

Institution of Incorporated Engineers
P Tootill IEng MIIE

Lighting Association
K R Kearney IEng MIIE

National Inspection Council for Electrical Installation Contracting

Office of the Deputy Prime Minister
K Bromley MIEE

Society of Electrical and Mechanical Engineers serving Local Government
C J Tanswell CEng MIEE MCIBSE

Author P R L Cook CEng FIEE

Preface

This book gives guidance on Part P (Electrical Safety) of the Building Regulations 2000 for England and Wales and on other parts of the Building Regulations that persons carrying out electrical installations will be expected to comply with.

The guidance is designed to provide information to meet:

- the competence requirements for a Principal Duty Holder and a Qualified Supervisor as required by Electrotechnical Assessment Scheme (EAS) Minimum Technical Competence of Enterprises (level A) that undertake Electrical Installation Work in Dwellings, and
- the competence requirements for a Level B operative for a limited scope (non-electrotechnical) enterprise defined in Part B of Electrotechnical Assessment Scheme (EAS) Framework for Minimum Technical Competence of Enterprises,
- the City & Guilds qualifications,
- the EMTA Awards Ltd Level 2 certificate for a domestic installer.

Domestic circuit schedules that comply with BS 7671: 2001(2004) Requirements for Electrical Installations (IEE Wiring Regulations 16th Edition) are described. They are not necessarily the most cost effective for any particular installation, but have the advantage of being simple and generally applicable.

Approved Documents are intended to provide guidance for some of the more common building situations. However, there may well be alternative ways of achieving compliance with the requirements. Thus there is no obligation to adopt any particular solution contained in an Approved Document if you prefer to meet the relevant requirement in some other way.

Legislation 1

- **Health and Safety**
- **The Building Regulations of England and Wales**
- **Approved document P: Electrical safety**
- **Notification to Building Control**
- **P2 Provision of information**

1.1 Health and safety

1.1.1 Health and Safety at Work etc Act 1974

Apart from the common law general duty of care of everyone for his neighbour (including employees and anyone who might use the place of work), there is specific legislation with respect to safety at work, the most fundamental being the Health and Safety at Work etc Act 1974.

The Health and Safety at Work etc Act 1974 is comprehensive, and concerns health, safety and welfare at work, the control of dangerous substances and certain emissions into the atmosphere. Sections 2, 3 and 4 of the Health and Safety at Work etc Act 1974 put a duty of care upon both the employer, the employee and the self-employed to ensure the health, safety and welfare at work of all persons, employees and others using the work premises.

This Act empowers the Secretary of State to make regulations. The most relevant to electrical installation work are:

- Electricity at Work Regulations 1989
- The Management of Health and Safety at Work Regulations 1992
- Construction (Design and Management) Regulations 1994
- Provision and Use of Work Equipment Regulations 1998
- Personal Protective Equipment at Work Regulations 1992.

NOTE: Lack of knowledge of a regulation is no defence in law.
(Further information on legislation relevant to persons engaged in electrical installations is given in the IEE publications: the Commentary on the IEE Wiring Regulations and Electrical Maintenance.)

1.1.2 Electricity at Work Regulations 1989

The Electricity at Work Regulations SI 1989 No 635 impose duties on every employer, every employee and every self-employed person to ensure that the safety requirements of the regulations are met. The regulations are enacted to provide for the electrical safety of persons in the workplace. The requirements of Regulation 4 are:

1. All systems shall at all times be of such construction as to prevent, so far as is reasonably practicable, danger.
2. As may be necessary to prevent danger, all systems shall be maintained so as to prevent, so far as is reasonably practicable, such danger.
3. Every work activity including operation, use and maintenance of a system and work near a system, shall be carried out in such a manner as not to give rise, so far as is reasonably practicable, to danger.
4. Any equipment provided under these Regulations for the purpose of protecting persons at work on or near electrical equipment shall be suitable for the use for which it is provided, be maintained in a condition suitable for that use, and be properly used.

In practice all electrical systems shall be designed, installed and maintained in use so as to prevent danger. The scope of the Electricity at Work Regulations not only includes the fixed wiring of the electrical installation but also current-using equipment supplied from the fixed installation including appliances, computers, photocopiers, power drills, etc.

The Memorandum of Guidance on the Electricity at Work Regulations published by the Health and Safety Executive (publication HSR25) provides guidance on all aspects of the Regulations. With respect to design and installation of electrical systems it says that "The IEE Wiring Regulations is a code of practice which is widely recognised and accepted in the UK and compliance with it is likely to achieve compliance with the relevant aspects of the 1989 Regulations".

The scope of the Electricity at Work Regulations is much wider than BS 7671: Requirements for Electrical Installations in that they require:

- installations to be constructed so as to be safe; regulation 4(1), 5, 6, 7, 8, 9, 10, 11,12;
- installations to be maintained so as to be safe; regulation 4(2);
- associated work to be carried out safely; regulation 4(3), 13, 14, 15;
- work equipment provided to be suitable for the purpose; regulation 4(4);
- persons to be competent; regulation 16.

The Electricity at Work Regulations are also concerned with maintenance of the installation, training and competency of staff, good working practices and suitable equipment.

Compliance with BS 7671 should provide for compliance with the Building Regulations as applies to the fixed installation. Compliance with the recommendations in the IEE Code of Practice for In-Service Inspection and Testing of Electrical Equipment is intended to provide guidance on compliance with the Electricity at Work Regulations as they apply to current-using equipment such as appliances and electrical office equipment.

1.1.3 Construction (Design and Management) Regulations 1994

The Construction (Design and Management) Regulations 1994 apply generally to construction work. The basic requirement is that design and construction must take account of the health and safety aspects both in the construction phase of the work and during any subsequent maintenance. There are also requirements regarding the maintenance and repair of the construction at any time, including after construction work is completed, that is during use and during demolition.

There is a requirement to provide reasonably foreseeable information necessary for the health and safety of persons who will carry out maintenance, repairs and cleaning in the future. Consequently persons with such responsibilities for a building should request access to the health and safety file prepared for the construction to see if there are any particular problems associated with the maintenance and repair including electrical matters.

1.1.4 Provision and Use of Work Equipment Regulations 1998

The Provision and Use of Work Equipment Regulations require that work equipment including installations, is so constructed (or adapted) so as to be suitable for the purpose for which it is provided. Equipment must be inspected after installation and before use, at suitable intervals and after exceptional events e.g. fire, flooding, mechanical damage. Potentially dangerous machinery must be guarded. Where necessary, logs must be maintained and adequate training given to operators.

1.1.5 Personal Protective Equipment at Work Regulations 1992

The Personal Protective Equipment at Work Regulations require every employer to ensure that suitable personal protective equipment is provided to employees, as may be necessary. The equipment must take account of the risks, the environmental conditions, ergonomic requirements, the state of the health of the person or persons, it must fit and it must comply with any appropriate provisions or standards.

There is a requirement upon employees to use protective equipment provided in accordance with training and instruction received. Employees are required to report the loss of such equipment.

The requirements of this legislation does mean that proper records should be kept of protective equipment and a suitable procedure be set up for checking that employees still have the equipment necessary and that it is in good order. This does not in any way reduce the duty of the employee to advise the employer of any defects or deficiencies in the equipment or the training that he or she has received.

1.1.6 Electricity Safety, Quality and Continuity Regulations 2002, Statutory Instrument 2665

The main purpose of the Electricity Safety, Quality and Continuity Regulations is to provide for the safety of the electricity supply distribution system. That is for the safety of the general public and of persons working on the system. As the title implies the Regulations also have requirements for power quality and supply continuity.

There are many references to BS 7671.

The regulations require distributors prior to connection of new properties to obtain confirmation that the installation to be connected complies with the requirements of BS 7671 (Regulations 9(4) and 25(2) of the ESQCR).

Regulation 28 requires the distributor to provide on request a written statement of:

(a) the maximum prospective short-circuit current at the supply terminals;
(b) for low voltage connections, the maximum earth loop impedance of the earth fault path outside the installation;
(c) the type and rating of the distributor's protective device or devices nearest to the supply terminals;
(d) the type of earthing system applicable to the connection; and
(e) the number of phases, frequency and voltage.

Regulation 24(4) requires for new supplies, unless inappropriate for reasons of safety, the distributor to make available an earth connection. (This is almost always provided for in the UK by the provision of a PME (TN-C-S) supply.)

1.1.7 Construction (Health, Safety and Welfare) Regulations 1996

The Construction (Health, Safety and Welfare) Regulations 1996 add requirements to those found in the Construction (Design and Management) regulations concerning general site safety duties of the employer including the self employed. Employees have a duty to carry out their work safely. Guidance is given in HSE publication INDG220.

1.2 The Building Regulations of England and Wales

1.2.1 The Building Regulations 2000, Statutory Instrument No. 2531

The Building Regulations 2000, Statutory Instrument 2000 No. 2531, are made under powers provided in the Building Act 1984 and apply in England and Wales, that is not Scotland nor Northern Ireland. In Scotland the requirements of the Building Standards (Scotland) Regulations apply, in particular regulation 26.

The purpose of the Building Regulations is to provide for the health and safety of people in and around buildings and also provide for matters such as energy conservation and access and use.

In the Building Regulations "building work" means:

(a) the erection or extension of a building;
(b) the provision or extension of a controlled service or fitting in or in connection with a building;
(c) the material alteration of a building, or a controlled service or fitting;
(d) work required by regulation 6 (requirements relating to material change of use);
(e) the insertion of insulating material into the cavity wall of a building;
(f) work involving the underpinning of a building.

Regulation 4 of the Building Regulations 2000 as amended requires:

4. (1) Building work shall be carried out so that:
(a) it complies with the applicable requirements contained in Schedule 1 (Parts A to P); and
(b) in complying with any such requirement there is no failure to comply with any other such requirement.

(2) Building work shall be carried out so that, after it has been completed:
(a) any building which is extended or to which a material alteration is made; or
(b) any building in, or in connection with, which a controlled service or fitting is provided, extended or materially altered; or
(c) any controlled service or fitting, complies with the applicable requirements of Schedule 1 (Parts A to P) or, where it did not comply with any such requirement, is no more unsatisfactory in relation to that requirement than before the work was carried out.

The responsibility for compliance rests with the person carrying out the building work, which can include plumbing and electrical installations. The person carrying out the electrical installation is personally responsible for compliance. Persons employing others to carry out work should confirm who has responsibility for compliance with the Building Regulations. Should there be non-compliance, the owner of the building is likely to be served with the enforcement notice if the work does not comply with the Building Regulations.

1.2.2 The Building (Amendment No. 2) Regulations 2004 Statutory Instrument No. 1808

Amendment No. 2 introduced Part P into the Building Regulations complete with a definition of electrical installation.

Electrical installation means fixed electrical cables or fixed electrical equipment located on the consumer's side of the electricity supply meter. This is not the same as in BS 7671 (IEE Wiring Regulations 16th Edition) which is not mandatory in law but a British Standard giving the recommendations of the British Electro-Technical Committee and the IEE. For the purposes of providing practical guidance with respect to the requirements of the Building Regulations 2000 for England and Wales, the Secretary of State has issued a series of Approved documents including Part P Electrical safety.

Guidance is given on compliance with Approved Document P, Electrical Safety. However, advice is also provided in Chapter 10 on other Building Regulation requirements relevant to electricians carrying out electrical work as follows:

Part A (Structure): depth of chases in walls, and size of holes and notches in floor and roof joists;

Part B (Fire safety): fire safety of certain electrical installations; provision of fire alarm and fire detection systems; fire resistance of penetrations through floors and walls;

Part C (Site preparation and resistance to contaminants and moisture): moisture resistance of cable penetrations through external walls;

Part E (Resistance to the passage of sound): penetrations through floors and walls;

Part F (Ventilation): ventilation rates for dwellings;

Part L (Conservation of fuel and power): energy efficient lighting;

Part M (Access and facilities for disabled people): heights of switches and socket-outlets.

All the above are available from the ODPM website: http://www.odpm.gov.uk/

Persons responsible for work within the scope of Part P of the Building Regulations may also be responsible for ensuring other parts of the Building Regulations where relevant are complied with, particularly if there are no other parties involved with the work.

The Building Regulations (Regulation 4(2)) require that, on completion of the work, the building should be no worse in terms of the level of compliance with the other applicable Parts of Schedule 1 to the Building Regulations, including Parts A, B, C, E, F, L, and M.

For example, holes cut in a ceiling for a recessed luminaire (light fitting) might degrade a floor's performance in terms of its resistance to fire (Part B) and sound penetration (Part E) and this is not allowed.

Chasing of walls and drilling of joists must comply with Part A to ensure the building structure remains sound. Chapter 10 of this publication provides guidance.

1.3 Approved document P: Electrical safety

1.3.1 The requirements

Requirement	*Limits on application*
PART P ELECTRICAL SAFETY	
Design, installation, inspection and testing **P1.** Reasonable provision shall be made in the design, installation, inspection and testing of electrical installations in order to protect persons from fire or injury. **Provision of information** **P2.** Sufficient information shall be provided so that persons wishing to operate, maintain or alter an electrical installation can do so with reasonable safety.	The requirements of this Part apply only to electrical installations that are intended to operate at low or extra-low voltage and are – (a) in a dwelling; (b) in the common parts of a building serving one or more dwellings, but excluding power supplies to lifts; (c) in a building that receives its electricity from a source located within or shared with a dwelling; and (d) in a garden or in or on land associated with a building where the electricity is from a source located within or shared with a dwelling.

▲ **Figure 1.3** The Requirements of Part P of the Building Regulations

1.3.2 Scope of Part P

Part P applies to electrical installations in buildings or parts of buildings comprising:

(i) dwelling houses and flats;
(ii) dwellings and business premises that have a common metered supply – for example shops and public houses with a flat above with a common meter;
(iii) common access areas in blocks of flats such as corridors and staircases;
(iv) shared amenities of blocks of flats such as laundries and gymnasiums.

Part P applies also to parts of the above electrical installations:

(v) in or on land associated with the buildings – for example Part P applies to fixed lighting and pond pumps in gardens;
(vi) in outbuildings such as sheds, detached garages and greenhouses.

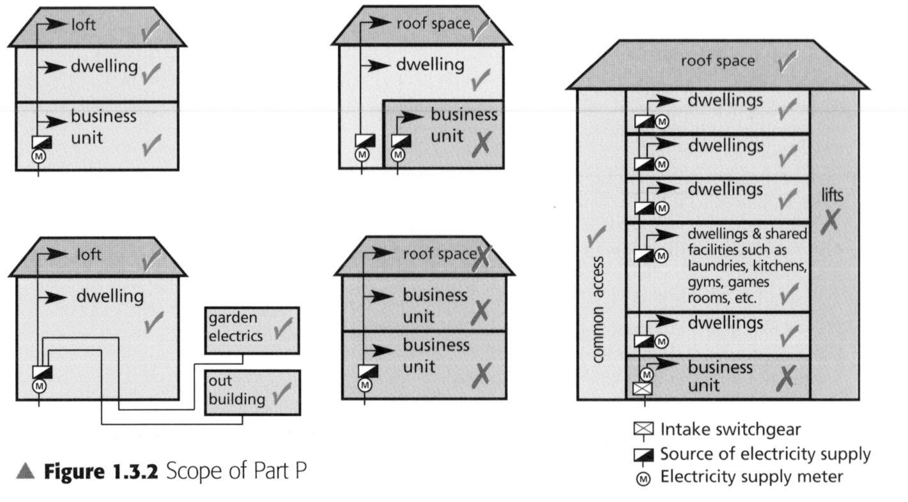

▲ **Figure 1.3.2** Scope of Part P

Part P does not apply to:

(i) business premises in the same building as dwellings with separate metering,
(ii) lifts in blocks of flats.

1.3.3 Compliance with Part P

In the Secretary of State's view, the requirements of Part P will be met by adherence to the 'Fundamental Principles' for achieving safety given in BS 7671 : 2001 Chapter 13. See Appendix A for the complete text.

To achieve these requirements electrical installations in dwellings etc. must be:

- designed and installed to afford appropriate protection against mechanical and thermal damage, and so that they do not present electric shock and fire hazards to people;
- susuitably inspected and tested to verify that they meet the relevant equipment and installation standards.

Chapter 13 of BS 7671 is met by complying with Parts 3 to 7 of BS 7671 except as allowed by Regulations 120-01-03 and 120-02. That is any intended departure from these Parts requires special consideration by the designer of the installation and is to be noted on the Electrical Installation Certificate specified in Part 7 (Regulation 120-01-03). Where the use of a new material or invention leads to departures from the Regulations, the resulting degree of safety of the installation is to be not less than that obtained by compliance with the Regulations. Such use is to be noted on the Electrical Installation Certificate specified in Part 7.

This publication is written to provide simple rules and installation requirements including circuit specifications for compliance.

1.4 Notification to Building Control

Except as below, the relevant Building Control body must be notified of all proposals to carry out electrical installation work in dwellings etc. (see section 1.3) before the work begins. The requirements of Part P apply to all electrical installation work in dwellings including any greenhouse, small detached building, conservatory, porch, covered yard or way and car port open on at least two sides. However, it is not always necessary to notify Building Control.

It is not necessary to give prior notification of proposals to carry out electrical installation work in dwellings to Building Control bodies if the work:

(a) is carried out by a registered competent enterprise, or
(b) is non-notifiable minor work.

1.4.1 Registered competent enterprise (Assessed enterprise)

Self-certification schemes
It is not necessary to give prior notification of proposals to carry out electrical installation work in dwellings to Building Control bodies if an assessed enterprise registered with an electrical self-certification scheme authorised by the Secretary of State undertakes the work. Such a registered competent enterprise may be called an assessed enterprise.

A list of the self-certification schemes with contact details is given in Appendix E. There are three levels of self-certification schemes:

Level A The requirements for an enterprise the scope of whose work includes the design, installation, inspection and testing of all electrical installation work that is associated with dwellings and is intended to operate at low or extra-low voltage

Level B The requirements for an enterprise the scope of whose work is limited to the design, installation, inspection and testing of defined electrical installation work, intended to operate at low or extra-low voltage, that is associated with dwellings and is undertaken in connection with, and ancillary to, some other non-electrical work. (See Annex 7 of Appendix D for an indicative list of non-electrical work).

Level C The requirements for an enterprise, the scope of whose electrical installation work is limited to minor electrical installation work intended to operate at low or extra-low voltage that is associated with dwellings and is undertaken in connection with, and ancillary to, some other non-electrical work. (See Annex 7 of Appendix D for an indicative list of non-electrical work.)

The requirements of these schemes are given in the document "Minimum Technical Competence of Enterprises that undertake Electrical Installation Work in Dwellings" prepared by the Electrotechnical Assessment Scheme. This is reproduced in Appendix D.

The assessed enterprise is responsible for ensuring compliance with BS 7671: 2001 and all relevant Building Regulations. On completion of the work, the assessed enterprise is required to formally notify its self-certification scheme in accordance with their procedures, who after checking competence to carry out the work will notify Building Control. The person ordering the work should also receive a duly completed Electrical Installation Certificate as or similar to the model in BS 7671. As required by BS 7671, the certificate must be made out and signed by the competent person or persons on behalf of the assessed (competent) enterprise that carried out the design, construction, inspection and testing work. Copies of relevant BS 7671 model forms are shown in Chapter 6 and guidance is given on inspection, testing and the completion of forms.

Electricians working on behalf of a competent enterprise are not required to notify Building Control in advance of work. The competent enterprise will notify their registration body on completion of the work. The registration body will notify Building Control. Electricians employed by competent enterprises but working on their own behalf and not registered individually with a self-certification scheme, are required to notify Building Control of any work within the scope of the Building Regulations they intend to carry out and Building Control will be required to arrange separate inspection and testing of their work.

Table 1 of Part P: Work that need not be notified to Building Control bodies
Work consisting of:
Replacing any electrical fitting including socket-outlets, control switches and ceiling roses
Replacing the cable for a single circuit only, where damaged, for example, by fire, rodent or impact[(a)]
Re-fixing or replacing the enclosures of existing installation components[(b)]
Providing mechanical protection to existing fixed installations[(c)]
Work that is not in a kitchen or special location and does not involve a special installation[(d)] and consists of:
Adding lighting points (light fittings and switches) to an existing circuit[(e)]
Adding socket-outlets and fused spurs to an existing ring or radial circuit[(e)]
Installing or upgrading main or supplementary equipotential bonding[(f)]
Work not in a special location on:
Telephone or extra-low voltage wiring and equipment for the purposes of communications, information technology, signalling, control and similar purposes

Notes

(a) On condition that the replacement cable has the same current-carrying capacity, follows the same route and does not serve more than one sub-circuit through a distribution board.

(b) If the circuit's protective measures are unaffected.

(c) If the circuit's protective measures and current-carrying capacity of conductors are unaffected by increased thermal insulation.

(d) Special locations and installations are listed in Table 2.

(e) Only if the existing circuit protective device is suitable and provides protection for the modified circuit, and other relevant safety provisions are satisfactory.

(f) Such work shall comply with other applicable legislation, such as the Gas Safety (Installation and Use) Regulations.

Table 2 of Part P: Special locations and installations[a]
Special locations:
Locations containing a bath tub or shower basin
Swimming pools or paddling pools
Hot air saunas
Special installations:
Electric floor or ceiling heating systems
Garden lighting or power installations
Solar photovoltaic (PV) power supply systems
Small scale generators such as microCHP units
Extra-low voltage lighting installations, other than pre-assembled, CE-marked lighting sets

Notes
[a] See IEE Guidance Note 7 which gives more guidance on achieving safe installations where risks to people are greater.

Similarly, members of institutions such as the Institution of Electrical Engineers (IEE) are not exempt from the requirement to notify Building Control of electrical work any more than a member of the Institution of Civil Engineers is exempt from the requirement to notify Building Control if he is carrying out foundation works in his own home.

1.4.2 Minor work

It is not necessary to give prior notification of proposals to carry out minor electrical installation work as described in Table 1 of Part P and does not include the provision of a new circuit.

Non-notifiable minor work

Work described in Table 1 is not to be notified to Building Control bodies.

However, non-notifiable work is also required to comply with Part P. Minor work must comply with BS 7671 including inspection and testing and the issue of a minor works certificate. As required by BS 7671, the certificate must be made out and signed by a competent person in respect of the inspection and testing of an installation. The competent person need not necessarily be a person registered with an electrical self-certification scheme, and may be a third party.

When the non-notifiable work is undertaken as DIY work, compliance with Part P is required. A way of showing compliance would be to follow the IEE guidance or guidance in other authoritative manuals that are based on this, and to have an electrician inspect and test the work and supply a Minor Electrical Installation Works Certificate. The electrician need not necessarily be registered with an electrical self-certification scheme but, as required by BS 7671, must be competent in respect of the inspection and testing of an installation.

In any event, non-notifiable works should also be drawn to the attention of the person carrying out subsequent work or periodic inspections. A way of doing this would be to supply Minor Electrical Installation Works Certificates covering the additions and alterations made since the original construction of the installation or since the most recent periodic inspection.

1.5 P2 Provision of information

The second requirement of Part P of the Building Regulations concerns the provision of information:

> P2. Sufficient information shall be provided so that persons wishing to operate, maintain or alter an electrical installation can do so with reasonable safety.

Meeting the requirements of BS 7671 will require the Installer to:

(i) Provide a schedule of inspections, schedule of tests, and electrical installation certificate or periodic inspection certificate (or minor works certificate if appropriate). See Chapter 6.

These must be provided to the person ordering the work with the intention that they be passed on to the householder.

(ii) Provide labelling of the installation. See Section 3.4.
(iii) Install cables in the building fabric only as permitted. See Section 2.3.

Design, selection and erection of electrical installations

2

- **Design**
- **Selection of materials**
- **Installation**

2.1 Design

2.1.1 New buildings (installations)

The Electricity Safety, Quality and Continuity Regulations 2002 require the electricity distributor to install the cut-out and meter in a safe location, where they are mechanically protected and can be safely maintained. In compliance with this requirement, the electricity distributor and installer may be required to take into account the risk of flooding. (Some guidance is given in the ODPM publication: Preparing for Floods, available from www.safety.odpm.gov.uk/bregs/floods/index.htm)

In accordance with the Electricity Safety, Quality and Continuity Regulations 2002 and the contract for a mains supply, proposals for new installations or significant alterations to existing ones must be agreed with the electricity distributor.

All new electrical installations including those in dwellings must comply with BS 7671. This guide provides uncomplicated examples of installations that will comply with BS 7671.

2.1.2 Additions and alterations to an installation

2.1.2.1 Electrical

BS 7671 requires in Regulation 130-07-01 that no addition or alteration, temporary or permanent, shall be made to an existing installation, unless it has been ascertained that the rating and the condition of any existing equipment, including that of the supplier, which will have to carry any additional load is adequate for the altered circumstances and the earthing and bonding arrangements are also adequate.

When carrying out an addition or alteration to an existing electrical installation, the installer must confirm that the old installation meets the current requirements of the Building

Regulations in so far as it affects the new installation and is adequate in all respects to supply the additional load if any; such that the new work is safe i.e. complies with Part 1 of BS 7671: Requirements for Electrical Installations.

In particular the rating and the condition of the existing equipment belonging to both the customer and the electricity distributor can:

- carry the additional load,
- provide adequate shock protection (loop impedances must be appropriate for the protective devices) and,
- the earthing and equipotential bonding arrangements are satisfactory.

Defects in the existing installation affecting the alteration or addition must be made good. Defects in the electrical installation identified during the work and not affecting the addition or alteration must be identified in writing to the person ordering the work.

2.1.2.2 Building works

Additions or extensions to a building must comply with the Building Regulations. If wiring is carried out in an extension to an existing building, the wiring to the extension must comply not only with Part P but also with all the other appropriate requirements of the Building Regulations. There is no particular requirement to ensure compliance with the Building Regulations with respect to other parts of the building not affected by the extension, alteration or addition. The compliance with the Building Regulations of the existing building must not be degraded. For example energy efficient luminaires must not be replaced by less efficient luminaires however insistent the customer may be. Walls and ceilings must not be degraded by chases, drillings, etc. (see Approved document A in Chapter 10 of this Guide for details).

2.1.2.3 Accessibility

Wall-mounted switches and socket-outlets should be located so that they are easily reachable where this is necessary to comply with Part M (Access to and use of buildings) of the Building Regulations. See Section 10. 7. Consumer units must be generally accessible for use by responsible persons in the household. They should not be installed where young children might interfere with them. See Section 3.1.

2.2 Selection of materials

2.2.1 The Building Regulations

The Building Regulations (regulation 7) require that building work shall be carried out:

(a) with adequate and proper materials which
  (i) are appropriate for the circumstances in which they are used,
  (ii) are adequately mixed or prepared, and
  (iii) are applied, used or fixed so as adequately to perform the functions for which they are designed; and

(b) in a workmanlike manner.

2.2.2 Compliance with equipment standards

Part 1 of BS 7671 requires that every item of equipment must comply with the appropriate EN or HD or National Standard implementing the HD. In the absence of an EN or HD the equipment must comply with the appropriate National Standard. In the UK a Harmonised Standard (EN) is published as a BS EN and where a Harmonised Document (HD) exists it will be incorporated into the National Standard (BS). In selecting equipment, care must be taken to ensure that there is a declaration from the supplier that the equipment complies with the appropriate British Standard.

When selecting equipment check that it is marked with the relevant British Standard number from the list in Appendix B.

Appendix B of this publication lists the British Standards referenced in BS 7671. It is a requirement of the Electrical Equipment Safety Regulations that before electrical equipment is put on sale, the manufacturer or authorised representative confirms that it complies with the safety requirements of the regulations. The manufacturer or authorised representative confirms that the equipment complies with all of the requirements of the appropriate European directives and indicates this by applying the CE mark.

Figure 2.2.2 CE mark

2.2.3 Independent certification schemes

For third party assurance that equipment complies with the appropriate British Standard, purchasers can look for an approval body mark such as the BSI kite mark or the ASTA/BEAB mark and for cables the British Approvals Service for Cables (BASEC) mark.

Figure 2.2.3.1 ASTA diamond mark

Figure 2.2.3.2 BASEC cable marks

Figure 2.2.3.3 BSI kite mark

2.3 Installation

2.3.1 Cable installation methods

The maximum conductor operating temperature the cable can withstand limits the current rating of a cable. The conductor temperature is determined by

i) the current and
ii) the thermal conductivity of the cable and its surroundings.

As a result the installation method of a cable affects its current-carrying capability. Standard installation Reference Methods have been determined and when selecting a standard circuit from Chapter 4 not only must the fuse or circuit-breaker type be known but also the installation Reference Method. The Reference Methods considered are:

- (M1) clipped direct to the surface, or embedded in plaster, Figure 2.3.1a
- (M3) installed in conduit or trunking on the surface, Figure 2.3.1b, 2.3.1c and 2.3.1d
- (M3) installed in conduit embedded in plaster, masonry or the like, Figure 2.3.1e
- (M6) in a thermally insulated wall or ceiling and in contact with the wall or ceiling on one side, Figure 2.3.1f and 2.3.1g
- (M6) installed in conduit or trunking in a thermally insulated wall or ceiling and in contact with the wall or ceiling on one side, Figure 2.3.1h
- totally enclosed in thermal insulation for more than 0.5 m, Figure 2.3.1i.

Note

Cables should not be totally surrounded by thermal insulation. If cables are totally surrounded by thermal insulation cable sizes may need to be increased and this may result in practical problems in terminating the cables in accessories. For this reason it is recommended that where practicable, precautions are taken to prevent cables being totally enclosed.

The installation reference methods are described below.

Reference method 1 (M1)

Sheathed cables, armoured or unarmoured, clipped direct or embedded in plaster

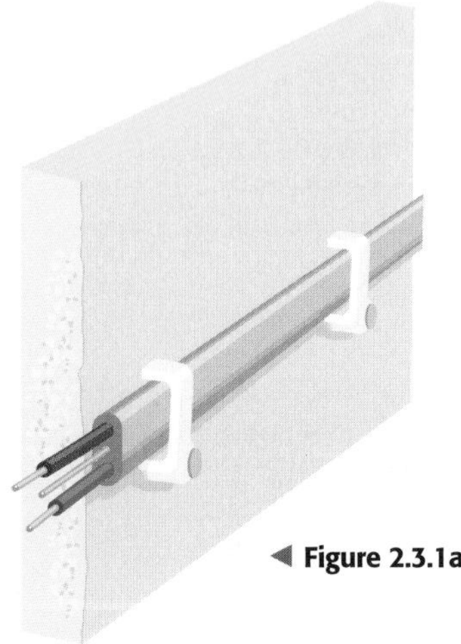

Figure 2.3.1a

Reference method 3 (M3)

Single-core or insulated and sheathed cables run in conduit or trunking

▲ Figure 2.3.1c

▲ Figure 2.3.1b

▲ Figure 2.3.1e

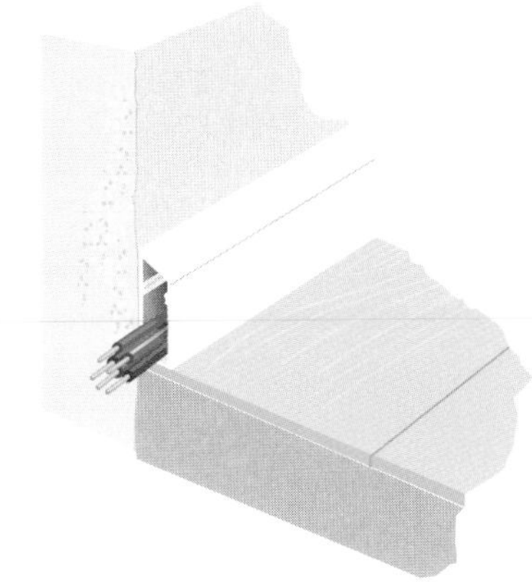

▲ Figure 2.3.1d

Reference method 6 (M6)

Multicore thermoplastic insulated and sheathed flat twin cable with protective conductor in an insulating wall and also in conduit in an insulating wall, the cable or conduit being in contact with a thermally conductive surface on one side; and single-core thermoplastic (pvc) insulated cables enclosed in conduit in a thermally insulating wall, the conduit being in contact with a thermally conductive surface on one side (Method 15).

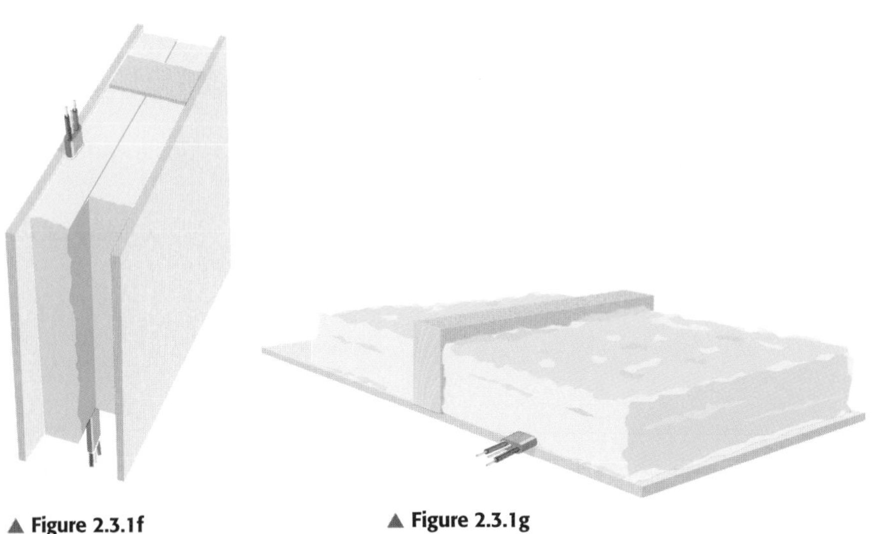

▲ **Figure 2.3.1f**

▲ **Figure 2.3.1g**

Surrounded by thermal insulation

If cables are surrounded by thermal insulation for less than 5 cm no derating is necessary. Where cables are totally enclosed the rating is half that for cables clipped direct to a conducting surface and unenclosed (Reference Method 1). It is preferable for the installation of cables to be so arranged that the cables are not totally enclosed. Reference Method 6 should be able to be achieved even in a modern thermally insulated house.

▶ **Figure 2.3.1h and 2.3.1i**

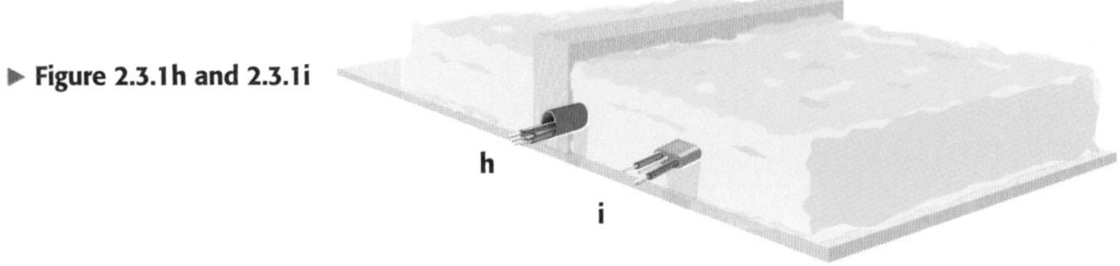

2.3.2 Floors and ceilings

When a cable is installed under a floor or above a ceiling it must be run in such a position that it is not liable to damage by contact with the floor or ceiling or their fixings. Unarmoured cables passing through a joist shall be at least 50 mm from the top or bottom as appropriate or enclosed in earthed steel conduit. Alternatively, the cables can be provided with mechanical protection sufficient to prevent penetration of the cable by nails, screws and the like. (Note, the requirement to prevent penetration can be difficult to meet.)

▼ **Figure 2.3.2** Cables through joists

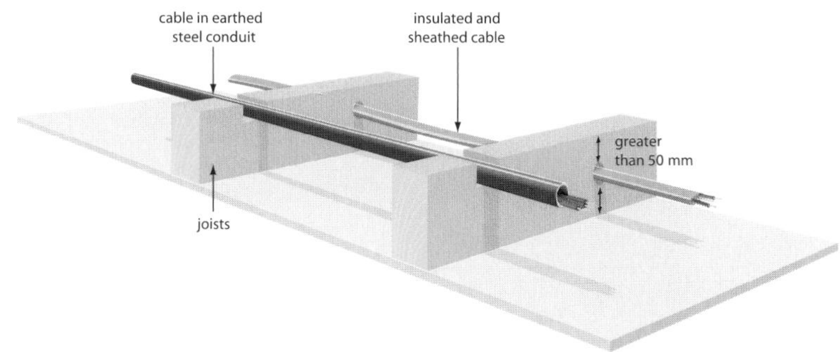

Notes:

1. Maximum diameter of hole should be 0.25 x joist depth.
2. Holes on centre line in a zone between 0.25 and 0.4 x span.
3. Maximum depth of notch should be 0.125 x joist depth.
4. Notches on top in a zone between 0.07 and 0.25 x span.
5. Holes in the same joist should be at least 3 diameters apart.

2.3.3 Walls

A cable installed in a wall or partition must be run in such a position or otherwise protected that it is not liable to be damaged by contact with the wall structure or construction fixings. This is particularly important when the wall or partition is metal or part metal construction. Care must be taken to ensure that when wall cladding, door frames etc are fixed cables are not damaged and metal structures made live.

Where a cable is concealed in a wall or partition at a depth of less than 50 mm from any surface it must be enclosed in earthed metal conduit (trunking or ducting) or installed either horizontally within 150 mm of the top of the wall or partition or vertically within

150 mm of the angle formed by two walls, or run horizontally or vertically to an accessory or consumer unit (see Figure 2.3.5).

Note:
A zone formed on one side of a partition wall of 100 mm or less thickness extends to the reverse side only if the location of the accessory can be determined from the reverse side.

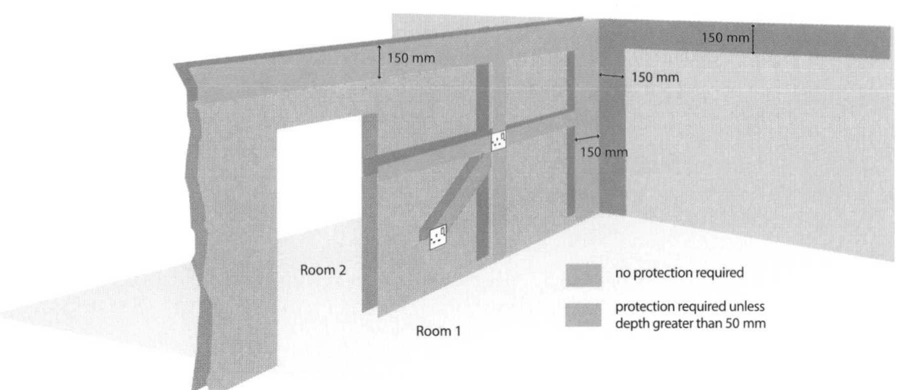

▲ **Figure 2.3.5** Permitted cable routes

Mains position 3

- **Location and acessibility**
- **Supply systems**
- **Earthing and equipotential bonding**
- **Labelling**
- **Installing Residual Current Devices (RCDs)**

3.1 Location and accessibility

The Electricity Safety, Quality and Continuity Regulations 2002 require the electricity distributor to install the cut-out and meter in a safe location, where they are mechanically protected and can be safely maintained.

In compliance with this requirement, the electricity distributor and installer may be required to take into account the risk of flooding. Distributor's equipment and the installation consumer unit/fuseboard should be installed above the flood level. Upstairs power and lighting circuits and downstairs lighting should be able to be installed above the flood level. Upstairs and downstairs circuits should have separate overcurrent devices (fuses or circuit-breakers).

Consumer units must be generally accessible for use by responsible persons in the household. They should not be installed where young children might interfere with them.

3.2 Supply systems

The Electricity Safety, Quality and Continuity Regulations require the electricity distributor (regulation 27) to advise of:

(a) the number of phases;

(b) the frequency; and

(c) the voltage,

and, on request, the distributor (regulation 28) to provide the following information:

(d) the maximum prospective short-circuit current at the supply terminals;

(e) for low voltage connections, the maximum earth loop impedance of the earth fault path outside the installation;

(f) the type and rating of the distributor's protective device or devices nearest to the supply terminals;

(g) the type of earthing system applicable to the connection.

This guide assumes:

(a) single-phase supply with

(b) 50 cycles per second frequency, and

(c) 230 V nominal voltage to earth.

(d) The maximum prospective short-circuit current is 16 kA at the supply terminals,

(e) the maximum external earth fault loop impedance (Ze) is 0.35 ohms for PME (TN-C-S) supplies and 0.8 ohms for cable sheath earth supplies (TN-S).

(f) A maximum distributor's protective device (cut-out fuse) rating of 100 A.

(g) See overleaf for earthing systems.

3.2.1 Protective Multiple Earthing (PME) supplies (TN-C-S system)

Almost all new supplies to dwellings will be from PME distribution systems. See Figure 3.2.1. The feature of such supplies is that the means of earthing for the installation is provided from the distributor's fused cut out where it is common with the PEN or neutral conductor. The size of the earthing and bonding conductors for standard domestic dwellings is given on the drawing. For non-standard installations, particularly larger installations, the sizes are tabulated (Table 3.3.2a).

Except in city centres the conditions assumed are that for a TN-C-S system:

- the maximum external earth fault loop impedance, Ze, is 0.35 ohms,
- the maximum prospective fault current is 16 kA.

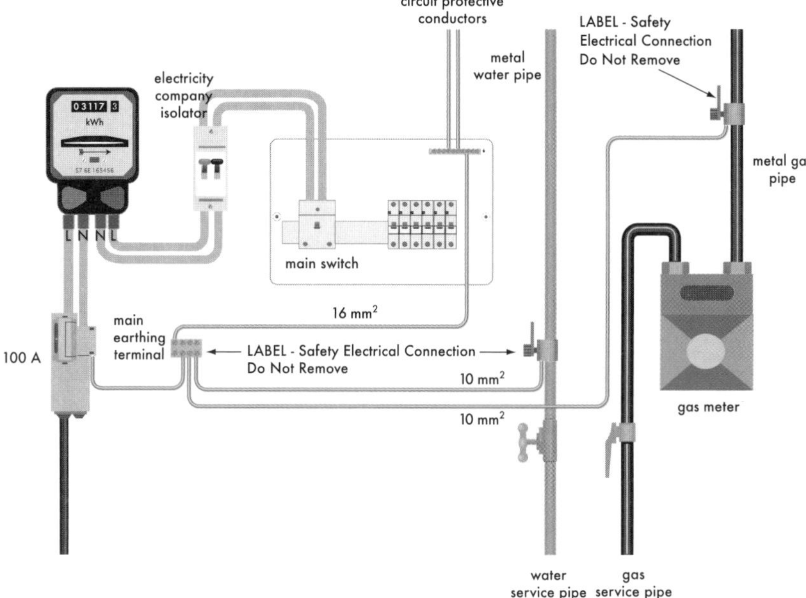

▲ **Figure 3.2.1** PME supply (TN-C-S system) Schematic of earthing and main equipotential bonding arrangements. Based on 25 mm^2 tails and selection from Table 54G.

Note: An isolator is not always installed by the electricity distributor.

Note:
Distributors will quote a Ze of 0.35 Ω and a fault level of 16 kA. A loop impedance of 0.35 Ω equates to a fault level of 230 V/0.35 Ω = 657 A. 16 kA is the worst case short-circuit fault level and 0.35 Ω worst case external earth loop impedance.

3.2.2 Cable sheath earth (TN-S system)

Cable sheath earths are identifiable by the earth connection being made to the cable sheath. This earth connection should be connected on to the sheath.

The distributor is responsible for this connection which should be securely and reliably made by a means such as soldering or brazing.

A maximum fault level of 16 kA may be assumed and a maximum external earth loop impedance of 0.8 ohm.

Main bonding and earthing conductor sizes for dwellings are given in Table 3.3.2b.

▼ **Figure 3.2.2** Cable sheath earth (TN-S system) Schematic of earthing and main equipotential bonding arrangements. Based on 25 mm² tails and selection from Table 54G.

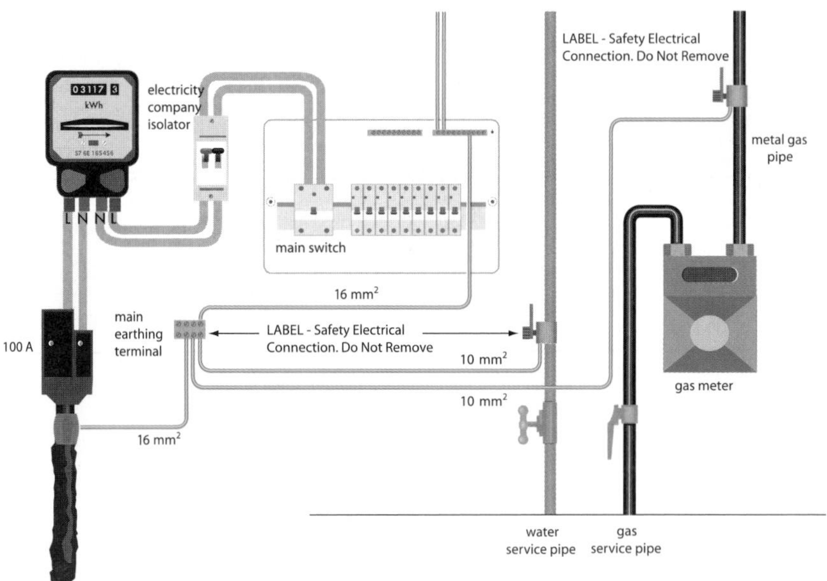

Note: An isolator is not always installed by the electricity distributor.

3.2.3 No earth provided (TT system)

TT installations will often be encountered in rural areas, where there are overhead supplies. Additionally, an installation forming part of a TT system may be encountered where a distributor may not be prepared to provide an earthing terminal for an installation such as that for a swimming pool, farm or building site. These installations are generally outside the scope of this Guide.

Figure 3.2.3 shows the mains position of a TT installation. It is necessary to install an earth electrode and it is recommended that the impedance to true earth of the electrode should not exceed 200 ohms. This can be checked by a loop impedance test when the supply has been connected.

Metal gas or metal water or other metal service pipes are not to be used as the earth electrode. A separate electrode must be installed. However metal, gas, water and other metal service pipes are required to be main bonded to the Main Earthing Terminal as shown in Figure 3.2.3.

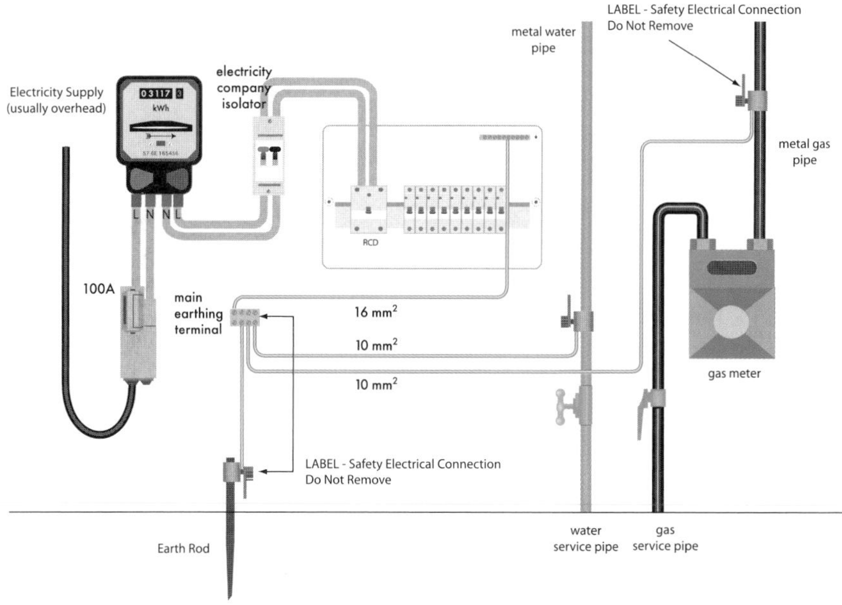

Note: An isolator is not always installed by the electricity distributor.

▲ **Figure 3.2.3** No earth provided (TT system). Based on 25 mm^2 tails and selection from Table 54G.

3.3 Earthing and equipotential bonding

3.3.1 Provision of an earth terminal

Unless inappropriate for reasons of safety, an electricity distributor is required when providing a new connection at low voltage (230 V/400 V) to make available an earthing terminal.

For new installations, the distributor will almost always provide a PME supply.

For dwellings, it would normally always be appropriate for an earthing terminal to be provided. For farms and swimming pools a PME supply may not be appropriate, and an installation forming part of a TT system should be employed.

3.3.2 Earthing conductor and main equipotential bonding conductors

Main equipotential bonding of metal services (Figures 3.2.1, 3.2.2, 3.2.3)

In each installation main equipotential bonding conductors are required to connect to the main earthing terminal, extraneous-conductive-parts including:

(i) water service pipes
(ii) gas installation pipes
(iii) other service pipes (e.g. oil) and ducting
(iv) central heating and air conditioning systems
(v) exposed metallic structural parts of the building
(vi) lightning protection systems.

Where an installation serves more than one building, the above requirement must be applied to each building.

Plastic supply pipes

There is no requirement to main bond an incoming service where both the incoming supply pipe and the pipework within the installation are both of plastic. Where there is a plastic incoming service and a metal installation within the premises, main bonding may be needed and in such cases the main bonding conductors should be connected on the customer's side of any meter, main stop cock or insulating insert.

Earthing and main equipotential bonding conductor cross-sectional areas

Except where PME conditions apply, the minimum cross-sectional area (csa) of the main equipotential bonding conductors is to be not less than half that of the earthing conductor. For a 100 A TN installation, the earthing conductor csa is normally 16 mm^2 and that of the main bonding conductors 10 mm^2 where the size of the supply neutral conductor is not more than 35 mm^2. However, in unusual circumstances electricity distribution network conditions may require larger conductors. For other conditions see Tables 3.3.2a and b.

When installing earthing and main equipotential bonding conductors:

(i) only copper conductors should be used; copper covered aluminium conductors or aluminium conductors or structural steel can only be used if special precautions outside the scope of this Guide are taken
(ii) bonding connections to incoming metal services should be as near as possible to the point of entry of the services to the premises, but on the consumer's side of any insulating section
(iii) the connection to the gas, water, oil, etc service should be within 600 mm of the service meter, or at the point of entry to the building if the service meter is external, and must be on the consumer's side before any branch pipework and after any insulating section in the service. The connection must be made to hard pipe, not to soft or flexible meter connections.
(iv) the connections must be made using suitable clamps (to BS 951) which will not be subject to corrosion at the point of contact
(v) if incoming gas and water services are of plastic, main equipotential bonding connections, if required, are to be made to metal installation pipes only.

TABLE 3.3.2a Protective conductor sizing for TN-C-S (PME) systems

Csa of supply neutral conductor	mm²	4	6	10	16	25	35	50	70
Csa of non-buried(1) earthing conductor(2)	mm²	10	10	10	16	16	16	25	35
Csa of main equipotential bonding conductors(3)	mm²	10	10	10	10	10	10	16	25

Notes to Table

1. In the event that the earthing conductor is buried (see Table 54A of BS 7671), it must have a csa of at least:
- 25 mm² copper or 50 mm² steel if not protected against corrosion by a sheath.
- 16 mm² copper or 16 mm² coated steel if protected against corrosion by a sheath but not protected against mechanical damage.

2. PME conditions apply, hence the csa of the earthing conductor must comply with the requirements of Section 543 and Section 547 of BS 7671. In the above Table, the csa of the earthing conductor has been selected in accordance with Table 54G and where applicable Table 54H.

3. The csa of the main equipotential bonding conductors is in accordance with Table 54H.

Where application of the regulations produces a non-standard size, a conductor having the nearest larger standard csa has been used in the above Table.

The above Table applies for copper conductors. Copper equivalent sizes may be used.

Electricity distributors may require conductors with a larger csa than that given above.

TABLE 3.3.2b Protective conductor sizing for TN-S and TT systems									
Csa of associated phase conductor[1]	mm²	4	6	10	16	25	35	50	70
Csa of non-buried[2] earthing conductor[3]	mm²	4	6	10	16	16	16	25	35
Csa of main equipotential bonding conductors[4]	mm²	6	6	6	10	10	10	16	25

Notes to Table

1. The phase conductor is the conductor between the origin of the installation and the consumer unit or main distribution board.
2. In the event that the earthing conductor is buried (see Table 54A), it must have a csa of at least:
   - 25 mm² copper or 50 mm² steel if not protected against corrosion by a sheath.
   - 16 mm² copper or 16 mm² coated steel if protected against corrosion by a sheath but not protected against mechanical damage.
3. The csa of the earthing conductor has been selected in accordance with Table 54G. Note that calculation is also permitted.
4. The csa of the main equipotential bonding conductors is in accordance with Regulation 547-02-01 of BS 7671.

Where application of the regulations produces a non-standard size, a conductor having the nearest larger standard csa has been used in the above Table.

The above Table applies for copper conductors. Copper equivalent sizes may be used.

Electricity distributors may require conductors with a larger csa than that given above.

Earthing

Every exposed-conductive-part (a conductive part of equipment which can be touched and which is not a live part but which may become live under earth fault conditions) must be connected by a protective conductor to the Main Earthing Terminal.

3.3.3 Supplementary equipotential bonding conductors

In certain special locations and in installations and locations of increased shock risk supplementary bonding is required, see Chapter 5. The cross-sectional areas of supplementary bonding conductors must comply with Table 3.3.3.

TABLE 3.3.3 Supplementary bonding conductor sizes

Size of protective conductor (mm²)	Minimum cross-sectional area of supplementary bonding conductors					
	Exposed-conductive-part to extraneous-conductive-part		Exposed-conductive-part to exposed-conductive-part		Extraneous-conductive-part to extraneous-conductive-part 1	
	mechanically protected (mm²) 1	not mechanically protected (mm²) 2	mechanically protected (mm²) 3	not mechanically protected (mm²) 4	mechanically protected (mm²) 5	not mechanically protected (mm²) 6
1.0	1.0	4.0	1.0	4.0	2.5	4.0
1.5	1.0	4.0	1.5	4.0	2.5	4.0
2.5	1.5	4.0	2.5	4.0	2.5	4.0
4.0	2.5	4.0	4.0	4.0	2.5	4.0
6.0	4.0	4.0	6.0	6.0	2.5	4.0
10.0	6.0	6.0	10.0	10.0	2.5	4.0
16.0	10.0	10.0	16.0	16.0	2.5	4.0

Note

If one of the extraneous-conductive-parts is connected to an exposed-conductive-part, the bonding conductor must be no smaller than that required for bonding conductors between exposed-conductive-parts and extraneous-conductive-parts as given in column 1 or 2.

3.4 Labelling

3.4.1 Earthing clamps

Bonding connections to metal pipes are made with earthing clamps to BS 951, complete with label as follows:

Safety Electrical Connection –
Do Not Remove

Permanent labels as above are required to be permanently fixed in a visible position at or near:

(i) the point of connection of every earthing conductor to an earth electrode or other means of earthing and

(ii) to the point of connection of every bonding conductor to an extraneous-conductive-part and

(iii) at the Main Earthing Terminal where it is separate from the main switchgear.

3.4.2 Switchgear and controlgear

Unless there is no possibility of confusion, a label indicating the purpose of each item of switchgear and controlgear must be fixed on or adjacent to the switchgear or controlgear. It may be necessary to label the item controlled as well as the controlgear.

3.4.3 Distribution boards (including consumer units)
Each protective device e.g. fuse or circuit-breaker must be arranged and labelled so that the circuit protected by the device can easily be identified.

3.4.4 Isolators
Switches used as isolators as well as being clearly identified must also indicate the circuit or circuits that they switch.

3.4.5 Equipment supplied from more than one source
Certain equipment may require the operation of more than one switch in order to make it safe. In such a case a durable warning notice must be permanently fixed in a clearly visible position to identify the appropriate devices.

3.4.6 Periodic inspection & testing
A notice of durable material indelibly marked with the words as follows must be fixed in a prominent position at or near the origin of the installation:

IMPORTANT

This installation should be periodically inspected and tested and a report on its condition obtained, as prescribed in BS 7671 Requirements for Electrical Installations published by the Institution of Electrical Engineers

Date of last inspection........................

Recommended date of next inspection.....................

3.4.7 Diagrams
A diagram or chart or schedule must be provided showing:

(i) The number of points, size and type of cable for each circuit
(ii) The method used to provide protection against indirect contact
(iii) The information necessary for the identification of each device performing the functions of protection, isolation and switching and its location
(iv) Any circuit vulnerable to an insulation test.

Circuits that may be vulnerable to insulation tests would be those that had solid-state devices such as burglar alarms or fire alarms, central heating controllers, solid state transformers etc.

3.4.8 Residual Current Devices

Where an installation incorporates an RCD a notice must be fixed in a prominent position at or near the origin of the installation as follows:

> The installation, or part of it, is protected by a device which automatically switches off the supply if an earth fault develops. Test quarterly by pressing the button marked 'T' or 'Test'. The device should switch off the supply and should then be switched on to restore the supply. If the device does not switch off the supply when the button is pressed, seek expert advice.

3.4.9 Warning notice: Non-standard colours

If alterations or additions are made to an installation so that some of the wiring complies with the harmonised colours and there is also wiring in the old colours, a warning notice must be affixed at or near the appropriate distribution board with the following wording:

> **CAUTION**
>
> This installation has wiring colours to two versions of BS 7671. Great care should be taken before undertaking extension, alteration or repair that all conductors are correctly identified.

3.4.10 Unexpected presence of nominal voltage exceeding 230 V

Where the nominal voltage exceeds 230 V to earth or 400 V between phases a warning label stating the maximum voltage present must be provided where it can be seen before gaining access to live parts.

3.4.11 Nominal voltage exceeding 230 volts (U or Uo) between simultaneously-accessible equipment

For simultaneously-accessible equipment with terminals or other fixed live parts having a nominal voltage (U or Uo) exceeding 230 volts between them, e.g. 400 V phase-to-phase, a warning label must be provided where it can be seen before gaining access to live parts.

3.4.12 Presence of different nominal voltages in the same equipment

Where equipment contains different nominal voltages, a warning label stating the voltages present must be provided so that it can be seen before gaining access to live parts.

3.5 Installing Residual Current Devices (RCDs)

3.5.1 Protection by an RCD

There are a number of instances where an installation is required to incorporate one or more RCDs (RCCBs or RCBOs). These instances include:

(i) where the external earth fault loop impedance is too high such that disconnection under earth fault conditions cannot be assured, for example where the distributor does not provide a means of earthing as in a TT system
(ii) for socket-outlet circuits in TT systems
(iii) for all socket-outlets that may reasonably be expected to supply portable equipment outdoors
(iv) for circuits supplying portable equipment for use outdoors by means of a flexible cable
(v) for socket-outlets in a room, other than a bathroom or shower room, containing a shower cubicle.

3.5.2 Applications of RCDs

Installations are required to be divided into circuits to avoid danger and minimise inconvenience in the event of a fault and to take account of hazards that might arise from the failure of a single circuit, e.g. a lighting circuit.

30 mA RCDs installed to provide protection to socket-outlets likely to feed portable equipment outdoors are normally installed to protect only those socket-outlets, see Figure 3a.

Where an RCD is fitted because the external earth loop impedance is too high for shock protection to be provided by an overcurrent device, for example in a TT system, the rated residual operating current should normally not be less than 100 mA. (Figures 3b, 3c and 3d).

If two RCDs are installed they should preferably control separate circuits, see Figure 3b, or a time delay type of 100 mA or greater RCD (S type) should be installed, see Figure 3c.

The use of RCBOs, see Figure 3d, will minimise inconvenience in the event of a fault.

The enclosures of RCDs or consumer units incorporating RCDs in TT installations should be of an all-insulated or Class II construction. Otherwise, additional precautions need to be taken to prevent faults to earth on the supply side of the RCD.

3.5.3 Applications of residual current circuit-breakers with overload current protection (RCBOs)

In TN systems protection against indirect contact may be provided by RCBOs operating as overcurrent devices. Maximum measured earth fault impedances, in ohms, are given in Table 2d of Appendix 2 of the On Site Guide. RCBOs are then providing protection against indirect contact as overcurrent devices and supplementary protection against direct contact as residual current devices.

When the designer intends that indirect shock protection is to be provided by a residual current circuit-breaker (RCCB) or the residual current element of an RCBO, loop impedances are as for an RCD, that is appropriate to the rated residual operating current (Zs less than or equal to 50 V/$I_{\Delta n}$), and not more than 200 ohms.

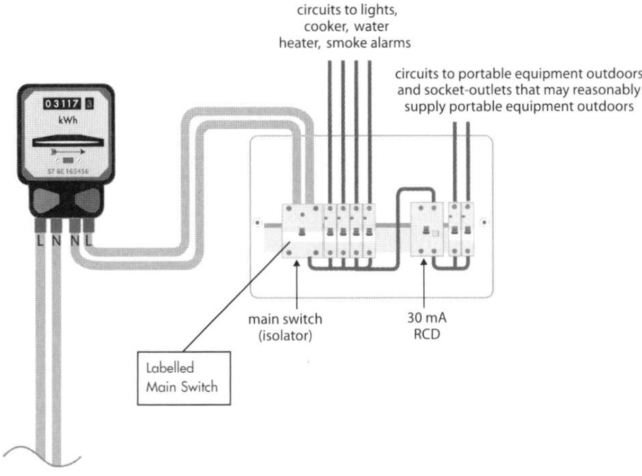

▲ **Figure 3a** Installing RCDs in a TN-S or TN-C-S installation

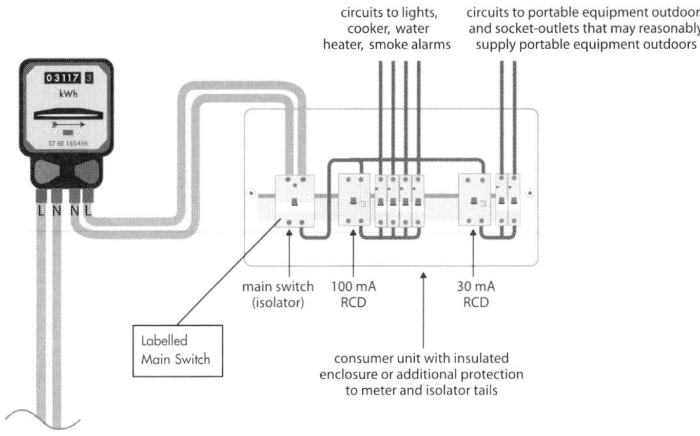

▲ **Figure 3b** Consumer unit with separate isolator

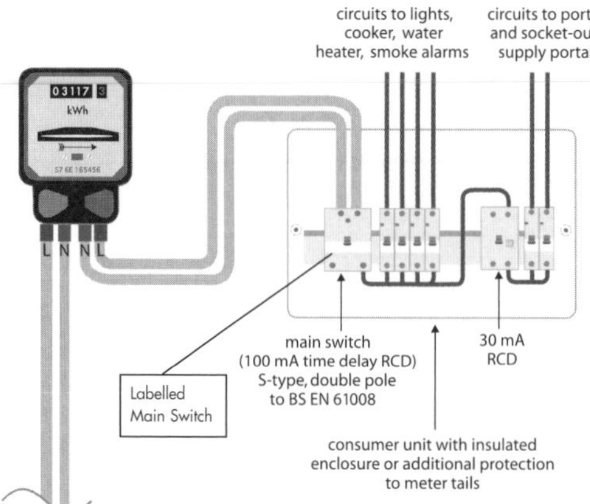

▲ **Figure 3c** Consumer unit using a time-delayed RCD as the main switch

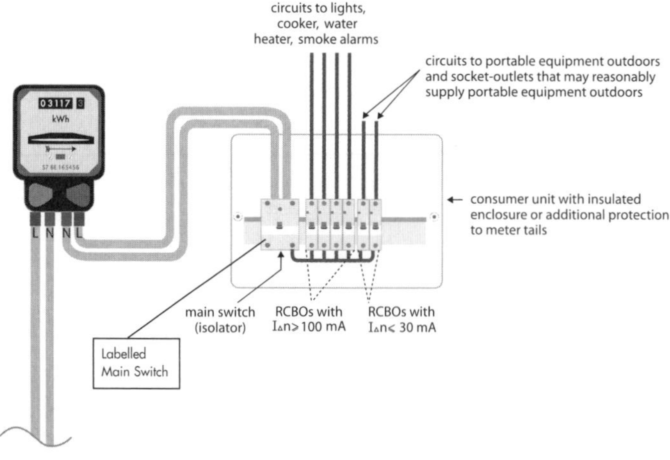

▲ **Figure 3d** Consumer unit with RCBOs

Note:
Residual current device (RCD) is a device type that includes residual current circuit-breakers (RCCBs), residual current circuit-breakers with integral overcurrent protection (RCBOs) and socket-outlets incorporating RCDs (SRCDs).

Circuit specifications 4

- **Standard circuits for installation methods 1, 3 and 6**
- **Final circuits using 13 A socket-outlets**
- **Permanently connected equipment: Requirements for switching**
- **Cooker circuits in household or similar premises**
- **Water and space heating**
- **Lighting circuits**

4.1 Standard circuits for installation methods 1, 3 and 6

The standard circuits have been designed for dwellings where the supply is at 230 V single-phase or 400 V three-phase.

The supply conditions assumed are those typical for the UK:

(i) the installation is supplied by

(a) a TN-C-S supply with a maximum external earth fault loop impedance, Ze, of 0.35 ohm, or
(b) a TN-S supply with a maximum Ze of 0.8 ohm, or
(c) a TT supply.

(ii) each final circuit is connected to a distribution board or consumer unit at the origin of the installation
(iii) the method of installation complies with Reference Methods 1, 3 or 6. See Chapter 2
(iv) the ambient temperature throughout the length of the circuit does not exceed 30 °C
(v) circuit lengths are "rounded" recognising the impracticality of exact measurement
(vi) if the maximum loop impedances are exceeded an RCD will be required to protect the circuit.
(vii) cables may be thermosetting (lsf) or thermoplastic (pvc).

Grouping of cables

Installing cables in proximity to other cables will reduce the current-carrying capacity Iz of the cable. The standard circuits in this Guide presume that the grouping of the circuits is no more onerous than described below. (For further guidance see Appendix 4 of the On Site Guide.)

(i) The circuit design permits any number of single-layer circuits when the spacing between adjacent surfaces of the cables exceeds one cable diameter, and, for other than semi-enclosed fuses to BS 3036 (rewirable), up to 5 touching, single-layer, circuits, when clipped to a non-metallic surface (Installation Method 1).

(ii) Up to four, 5 A or 6 A circuits of enclosed or bunched cables (Methods 3 and 6) are allowed for circuits protected by semi-enclosed fuses to BS 3036 and up to 6 circuits when protected by BS 88 or BS 1361 fuses or by circuit-breakers to BS 3871-1 or BS EN 60898 or RCBOs to BS EN 61009 or 6 A or 10 A lighting circuits protected by circuit-breakers or RCBOs.

(iii) For other groupings and/or high ambient temperatures, cable sizes will need to be increased. See the On Site Guide.

White and grey sheathed cables

Insulated and sheathed flat cables with bare protective conductor in the new harmonised cable colours are available in two types as follows:

White sheathed – thermosetting cable with low smoke (lsf) properties
Grey sheathed – pvc cable as previously available in the old cable colours.

Insulated and sheathed flat cables with bare protective conductor in the old cable colours may have white or grey sheaths, but they are always pvc cables.

Table 4.1.1. Standard domestic circuits with grey thermoplastic (PVC) or white thermosetting cable, installation methods 1, 3, 4, 6 and 15. Type B circuit-breaker to BS EN 60898, type B RCBO to BS EN 61009 and Type 1 mcb to BS 3871 (for existing installations).

				Maximum cable length		Maximum test loop impedance†	
Type of final circuit	Cable size pvc/pvc	Circuit-breaker rating	Max. floor area	TN-C-S PME earth Ze up to 0.35 Ω	TN-S sheath earth Ze up to 0.8 Ω	Type B BS EN 60898/BS EN 61009	Type 1 BS 3871
	mm²	A	m²	m	m	Ω	Ω
Ring, supplying 13 A socket-outlets	2.5/1.5	32	100	90	90	1.2	1.5
Radial, supplying 13 A socket-outlets	2.5/1.5	20	50	30	30	1.92	2.4
Cooker (oven+hob) control unit with socket-outlet	6/2.5	32	-	40	40	1.2	1.5
Cooker (oven+hob) control unit with no socket-outlet	6/2.5	32	-	40	40	1.2	1.5
Oven (no hob)	2.5/1.5	16	-	30	30	2.4	3.0
Immersion heater	2.5/1.5	16	-	30	30	2.4	3.0
Shower to 30 A (7.2 kW)	6/2.5	32	-	40	40	1.2	1.5
Shower to 40 A (9.6 kW)	10/4	40	-	40	40	0.96	1.20
Storage radiator	2.5/1.5	16	-	30	30	2.4	3.0
Fixed lighting	1.5/1.0	10	-	100*	100*	3.84	4.8

*100 m cable including switch drops, 35 m loop on length
† Measured values at an ambient temperature of 10° C to 20° C

Table 4.1.2 Standard domestic circuits grey thermoplastic (PVC) or white thermosetting cable installation methods 1, 3, 4, 6 and 15. Type C circuit-breaker to BS EN 60898, type C RCBO to BS EN 61009 and Type 3 mcb to BS 3871-1

				Maximum cable length		Maximum test loop impedance†
Type of final circuit	Cable size pvc/pvc	Circuit-breaker rating	Max. floor area	TN-C-S PME earth Ze up to 0.35 Ω	TN-S sheath earth Ze up to 0.8 Ω	Type C and type 3
1	2	3	4	5	6	7
	mm²	A	m²	m	m	Ω
Ring, supplying socket-outlets	2.5/1.5	32	100	70	90 with RCD	0.60
Radial, supplying socket-outlets	2.5/1.5	20	50	30	20	0.96
Cooker (oven+hob) control unit with socket-outlet	6/2.5	32	-	30	40 with RCD	0.60
Cooker control unit, no socket-outlet	6/2.5	32	-	30	40 with RCD	0.60
Oven (no hob)	2.5/1.5	16	-	30	30	1.20
Immersion heater	2.5/1.5	16	-	30	30	1.20
Shower to 30 A (7.2 kW)	6/2.5	32	-	35	35 with RCD	0.60
Shower to 40 A (9.6 kW)	10/4	40	-	32	32 with RCD	0.48
Storage radiator	2.5/1.5	16	-	30	30	1.20
Fixed lighting	1.5/1.0	10	-	100*	100*	1.92

Notes

RCD The maximum earth fault loop impedance of column 7 may be exceeded if Ze is approaching 0.8 ohms and then an RCD will be required. See section 3.5. A 30 mA RCD for socket-outlets circuits and 100 mA for other circuits would be appropriate.

*100 m cable including switch drops, 35 m loop on length

† Measured values at an ambient temperature of 10° C to 20° C

Table 4.1.3 Standard domestic circuits grey thermoplastic (PVC) or white thermosetting cable, installation methods 1, 3, 4, 6 and 15. Cartridge fuse to BS 1361

				Maximum cable length		Maximum test loop impedance†
Type of final circuit	Cable size pvc/pvc	Fuse rating	Max. floor area	TN-C-S PME earth Ze up to 0.35 Ω	TN-S sheath earth Ze up to 0.8 Ω	
	mm^2	A	m^2	m	m	Ω
Ring, supplying socket-outlets	2.5/1.5	30	100	90	90	0.96
Radial, supplying socket-outlets	2.5/1.5	20	50	28	28	1.42
Cooker, control unit with socket-outlet	6/2.5	30	-	42	31	0.96
Cooker, control unit with no socket-outlet	6/2.5	30	-	42	42	1.54
Immersion heater	2.5/1.5	15	-	40	40	4.18
Shower to 30 A (7.2 kW)	6/2.5	30	-	40	40	1.54
Shower to 40 A (9.6 kW)	10/4	45	-	50	10	0.8
Storage radiator	2.5/1.5	15	-	35	35	4.18
Fixed lighting	1.5/1.0	5	-	100*	100*	13.68

*100 m cable including switch drops, 35 m loop on length

† Measured values at an ambient temperature of 10° C to 20° C

Table 4.1.4 Standard domestic circuits thermosetting (white) cable only, installation methods 1 and 3 only. Rewireable fuse to BS 3036

				Maximum cable length		Maximum test loop impedance†
Type of final circuit	Cable size pvc/pvc	Fuse rating	Max. floor area	TN-C-S PME earth Ze up to 0.35 Ω	TN-S sheath earth Ze up to 0.8 Ω	
	mm²	A	m²	m	m	Ω
Ring, supplying socket-outlets	2.5/1.5	30	100	90	90	0.91
Radial, supplying socket-outlets	2.5/1.5	20	50	NP	NP	1.48
Cooker, control unit with socket-outlet	6/2.5	30	-	40	40	0.91
Cooker control unit with no socket-outlet	6/2.5	30	-	40	40	2.21
Immersion heater	2.5/1.5	15	-	40	40	4.46
Shower to 30 A (7.2 kW)	6/2.5	30	-	40	40	2.21
Shower to 40 A (9.6 kW)	10/4	45	-	50	50	1.33
Storage radiator	2.5/1.5	15	-	35	35	4.46
Fixed lighting	1.5/1.0	5	-	71*	71*	14.80

*71 m cable including switch drops, 35 m loop on length
NP = Not Possible
† Measured values at an ambient temperature of 10° C to 20° C

4.2 Final circuits using 13 A socket-outlets (to BS 1363-2) and fused connection units (to BS 1363-4)

4.2.1 General

In domestic premises a ring or radial socket-outlet final circuit, with spurs and permanently connected equipment, if any, may supply an unlimited number of socket-outlets and fused connection units within the area given in the standard circuit tables.

Socket-outlets for washing machines, tumble dryers and dishwashers should be located so as to provide reasonable sharing of the load in each leg of the ring. Consideration should be given to a separate ring final circuit in the kitchen.

Where two or more ring final circuits are installed the socket-outlets and permanently connected equipment to be served are to be reasonably distributed among the circuits.

4.2.2 Spurs

The total number of fused spurs is unlimited but the number of non-fused spurs should not exceed the total number of socket-outlets and items of stationary equipment connected directly in the circuit.

A non-fused spur feeds only one single or one twin or multiple socket-outlet or one permanently connected item of equipment. Such a spur is connected to a circuit at the terminals of a socket-outlet or junction box or at the origin of the circuit in the distribution board.

A non-fused spur is wired in the same size (cross-sectional area) cable as the ring final circuit.

A fused spur is connected to the circuit through a fused connection unit, the rating of the fuse in the unit not exceeding that of the cable forming the spur and, in any event, not exceeding 13 A.

4.3 Permanently connected equipment: Requirements for switching

Equipment permanently connected to a socket-outlet circuit and not exceeding 13 A rating should be locally protected by a fuse of rating not exceeding 13 A (to BS 1362) or by a circuit-breaker of rating not exceeding 16 A and controlled by a readily accessible switch in the fixed installation (e.g. switched fused connection unit). A separate switch is not required where a local circuit-breaker is used.

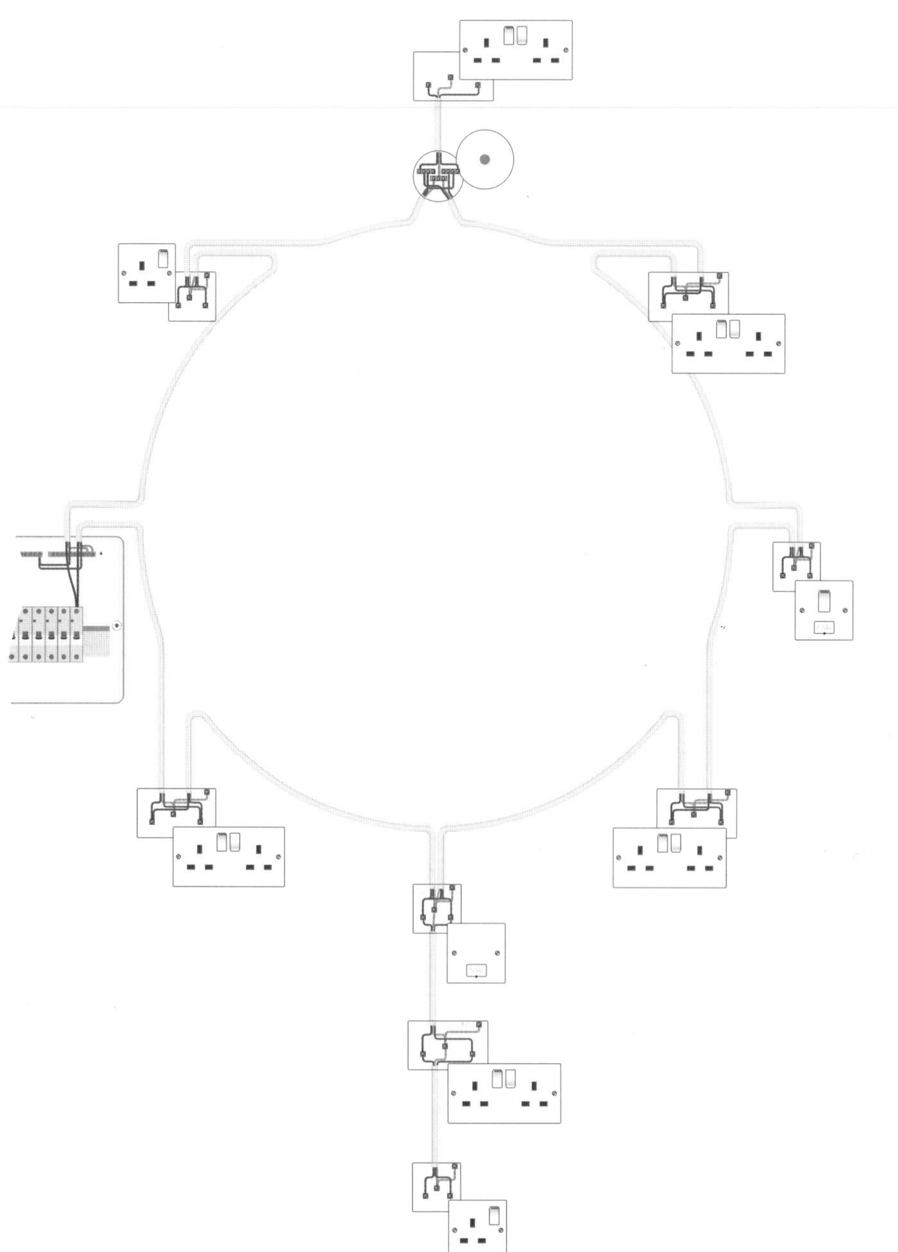

▲ **Figure 4.3** Ring final circuit supplying socket-outlets and an item of permanently connected equipment

Fixed or stationary appliances exceeding 13 A rating which may give rise to a hazard should be provided with a means of switching off. The switch should not be placed as to put the operator in danger. The switch should be in a readily accessible position. Where two or more such appliances are installed in the same room, one interrupting means may be used to control all the appliances.

Each switch or circuit-breaker used for isolation must be identified by position or durable marking to indicate the equipment controlled.

4.4 Cooker circuits in household or similar premises

The circuit supplies a control switch complying with BS 3676 or a cooker control unit complying with BS 4177 (which incorporates a socket-outlet).

The rating of the circuit is determined by the assessment of the current demand of the cooking appliance(s), and cooker control unit socket-outlet if any. A 30 or 32 A circuit is usually appropriate for household or similar cookers of rating up to 15 kW.
A circuit of rating exceeding 15 A but not exceeding 50 A may supply two or more cooking

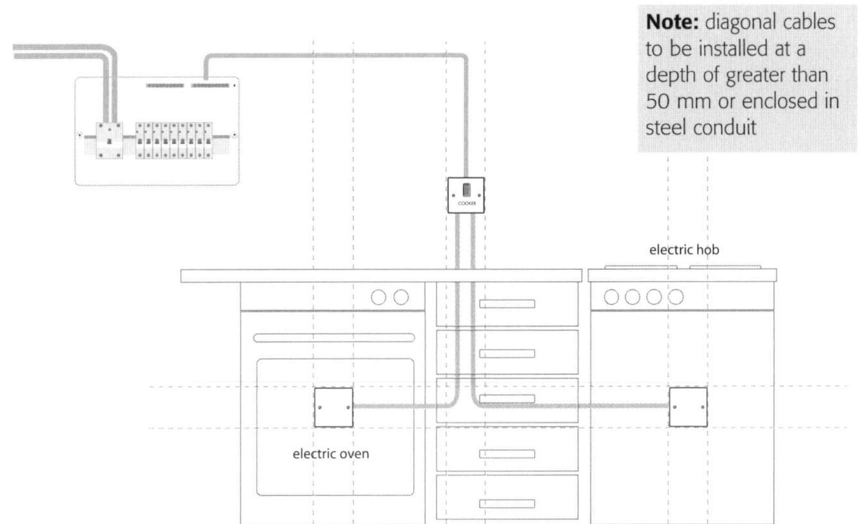

▲ **Figure 4.5** Cooker circuit

▲ **Figure 4.7** Domestic lighting circuit

appliances where these are installed in one room. The control switch or cooker control unit should be placed within two metres of the appliance, but not directly above it. Where two stationary cooking appliances are installed in one room, one switch may be used to control both appliances provided that neither appliance is more than two metres from the switch.

It is recommended that electric ovens are supplied by a separate circuit; however, for lightly loaded circuits ovens of rating 13 A or less may be connected into a ring final circuit.

Precautions need to be taken to prevent the heat generated by a cooker, including the hob, creating a risk of fire, or of harmful thermal effects, to adjacent equipment or materials including furnishings e.g. curtains.

See Section 5.2 for location of accessories in kitchens.

4.5 Water and space heating

A Water heater fitted to a storage vessel in excess of 15 litres capacity, or a permanently connected heating appliance forming part of a space heating installation, should be supplied by its own separate circuit. (And not supplied from a ring final circuit.)

Immersion heaters should be supplied through a switched flex-outlet connection-unit (to BS 1363-4) or a double pole switch with flex outlet complying with BS EN 60669-1 or BS EN 60669-2-4.

Instantaneous water heaters (including showers) of rating exceeding 3 kW should be supplied by a separate circuit. (Please see standard circuits.) Local isolation of water and electricity should be provided to facilitate maintenance.

Instantaneous water heaters including showers must comply with BS EN 60335-2-35. Check they are water protected to a minimum IPX4. Shower pumps must comply with BS EN 60335-2-41 and once again should be protected to a minimum of IPX4 rating.

4.6 Lighting circuits

See the Tables in this Section for specifications for domestic circuits and Figure 4.7 for circuits wired in the harmonised colours and see also Figures 11.3 and 11.4.

Special installations, special locations and kitchens 5

- Introduction
- Kitchens
- Locations containing a bath or shower
- Swimming pools
- Hot air saunas
- Floor and ceiling heating
- Garden lighting and power, sheds and garages
- Builders supplies

5.1 Introduction

The Wiring Regulations BS 7671

Special installations or locations in BS 7671 terminology are those installations or locations where there are additional requirements. The additional requirements for example might be to protect against environmental conditions such as water and steam and to provide adequate protection against electric shock in situations where the body is more susceptible i.e. without clothes or immersed in water or in contact with Earth.

Part P of the Building Regulations

In Approved document P certain of the special locations of BS 7671 are identified together with kitchens as locations where the relaxation allowing minor works to be carried out without notifying Building Control are not applicable. Only replacement of equipment including accessories can be carried out without notification. See Table 1 of Chapter 1.

This Chapter briefly describes the additional precautions to be taken in kitchens and the special locations and installations found in dwellings, that is for installations within the scope of Part P of the Building Regulations. For further information on special locations including those outside the scope of the Building Regulations, refer to IEE Guidance Note No 7 and the Commentary on the Wiring Regulations.

Special locations and installations from Table 2 of Approved document P

- Locations containing a bath tub or shower basin
- Swimming pools or paddling pools
- Hot air saunas

- Electric floor or ceiling heating systems
- Garden lighting or power installations
- Solar photovoltaic (PV) power supply systems
- Small scale generators such as microCHP units
- Extra-low voltage lighting installations, other than pre-assembled, CE-marked lighting sets.

5.2 Kitchens

Kitchen is defined in the Building Regulations as a 'room or part of a room which contains a sink and food preparation facilities'.

In open plan areas the zone of a kitchen may be considered to extend from the edge of the sink to a distance of 3 m or to a nearer dividing wall.

5.2.1 Introduction

A kitchen is particularly identified in the Approved document as being a location where:

- adding a lighting point, light fitting and switches to an existing circuit
- adding socket-outlets and fused spurs to existing ring or radial circuit
- installing or upgraded main or supplementary equipotential bonding

is required to be notified to Building Control. (In the case of the work being performed by a registered competent firm, the certification body, on completion of the work, will notify Building Control.)

As far as BS 7671 is concerned a kitchen is not a special location. However, the work in installing a fitted kitchen can be fairly substantial, involving plumbing, ventilation and significant alterations to the electrical installation. If additional kitchen appliances and luminaires (lights) are installed new socket-outlet and lighting circuits may be required.

5.2.2 Location of accessories in kitchens

General guidance can be provided as follows:

(i) Wiring accessories (e.g. socket-outlets, switches) should be mounted on the building fabric and not on kitchen furniture

(ii) Cooker control switches, extractor fan switches, etc should not be mounted so that it is necessary to lean or reach over gas or electric hobs for their operation

(iii) Socket-outlets should be installed a minimum of 450 mm from the floor

(iv) Accessories should be installed a minimum of 300 mm from the edge of kitchen sinks and draining boards to reduce the risk of being splashed

(v) Socket-outlets supplying washing machines and dishwashers etc, should be positioned so that water that may drip from plumbing or the equipment is unlikely to affect the socket-outlet or plug.

(vi) To prevent damage to the plug top and flexible cable on insertion and withdrawal the centre of a socket-outlet should be a minimum of 150 mm above the work surface.

(vii) Socket-outlets supplying appliances pushed under a work-surface eg. dishwashers, tumble dryers and fridges should be accessible when the appliance is pulled out.

(viii) Appliances built into kitchen furniture (integrated appliances) should be connected to a socket-outlet or fused connection unit that is readily accessible when the appliance is in place and in normal use or supplied from a socket-outlet or other connecting device controlled by a readily accessible double pole switch or switched fused connection unit.

(ix) Light switches should be readily accessible.

(x) Manufacturer's instructions should be followed.

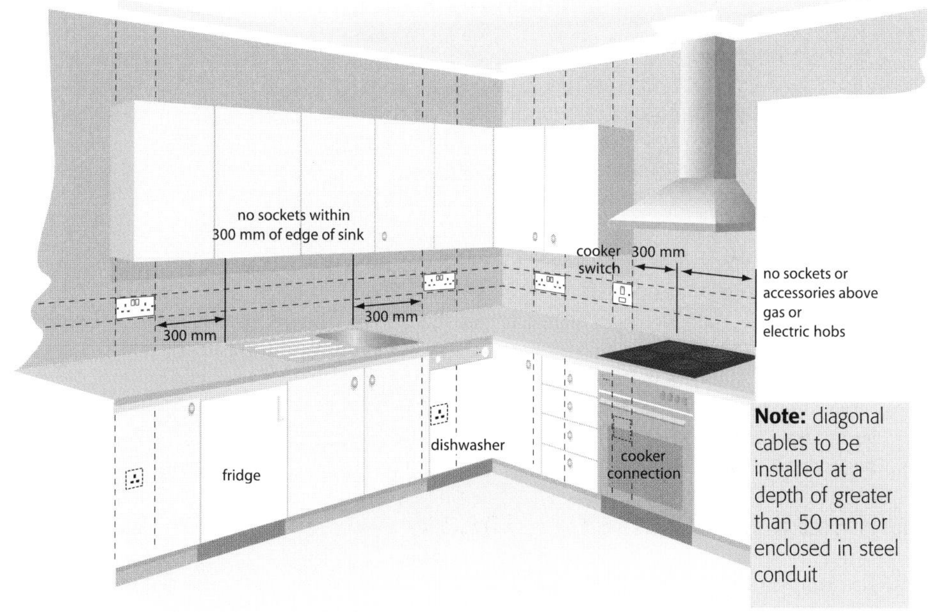

▲ **Figure 5.2** Kitchen installation

Note: Metal waste pipes in contact with Earth may be extraneous-conductive -parts and should be main bonded back to the Main Earthing Terminal.

5.2.3 Supplementary bonding in kitchens

There is no specific requirement in BS 7671 to provide supplementary bonding in kitchens. Water pipes, metal sinks or draining boards and metal furniture do not require supplementary bonding.

5.2.4 Not requiring notification to Building Control

The replacement of an accessory, such as a socket-outlet, switch, ceiling rose or light fitting does not require notification to Building Control. The addition of lighting points to an existing circuit, the addition of sockets-outlets and fused spurs as would be required for installing a fitted kitchen, must be notified to Building Control unless performed a registered competent enterprise or person.

To summarise, when new kitchen fittings are installed the electrical work must be carried out by a competent firm or Building Control must be notified in advance for inspection and testing on completion.

5.3 Locations containing a bath or shower

5.3.1 Introduction

Special precautions are required in locations containing a bath or shower, including shower rooms, en-suite showers and bedrooms with a bath or a shower. Bedrooms with a shower enclosure are covered in Section 5.3.2.

The additional requirements are summarised below:

(i) Socket-outlets, other than shaver supply units complying with BS EN 60742 Chapter 2, Section 1 are not allowed in the location (but see requirements for shower cubicles in bedrooms in Section 5.3.2).

(ii) Supplementary bonding is required within the zones. This requires supplementary bonding cables connecting an earth terminal of each circuit supplying equipment in the zones to extraneous-conductive-parts including:

- Metal water and waste pipes (including central heating)
- Accessible metal structural parts of the building
- Metal baths and shower basins
- Air conditioning systems.

The supplementary bonding is to be carried out in or in close proximity to the zones. It could be carried out in an adjacent airing cupboard (see Figure 5.3) or above a ceiling or under floorboards.

(iii) Equipment installed in zones 0, 1, 2 and 3 must have suitable additional protection against the ingress of water, see Table 5.3.

(iv) There are restrictions on the installation of current-using equipment, switchgear and wiring accessories (see Table 5.3 and Figure 5.3a)

(v) The cables of underfloor heating installations must be covered by an earthed metallic grid or the heating cable should have an earthed metallic sheath. Supplementary bonding is required.

Table 5.3 Requirements for current-using equipment, switchgear and accessories in a location containing a bath or shower

Zone	Requirements for equipment in the zones		
note 2	**Minimum degree of protection**	**Fixed current-using equipment**	**Switchgear and accessories**
0	IPX7	Only SELV fixed equipment that cannot be located elsewhere	None allowed
1	IPX4 IPX5 if water jets	SELV equipment allowed. Water heaters, shower pumps, allowed. Other fixed equipment e.g. luminaires and fans that cannot reasonably be located elsewhere are allowed if protected by a 30 mA RCD.	Only 12 V a.c. and 30 V d.c. switches of SELV circuits allowed, the safety source being installed outside zones 0, 1 and 2.
2	IPX4 (but shaver supply units complying with BS EN 61558-2-5 allowed when protected from direct shower spray) IPX5 if water jets	SELV equipment allowed. Water heaters, shower pumps, luminaires, fans, heating appliances, units for whirlpool baths allowed. Other fixed equipment that cannot reasonably be located elsewhere allowed.	SELV switches and SELV socket-outlets allowed, the safety source being outside zones 0, 1 and 2, and shaver supply units to BS EN 60742 Chapter 2 Section 1 allowed only if fixed where direct spray from showers is unlikely
3	General requirements IPX5 if water jets	SELV equipment allowed. Appliances allowed and, unless fixed, must be protected by a 30 mA RCD.	Accessories allowed except for socket-outlets. There is to be no provision for connecting portable equipment. SELV socket-outlets and shaver supply units to BS EN 60742 Chapter 2 Section 1
Outside Zones	General requirements	General requirements	Accessories allowed except for socket-outlets. SELV socket-outlet and shaver supply units to BS EN 60742 Chapter 2 Section 1

Note 1: Where a shower cubicle is installed in a room other than a bathroom or shower room, outside of zones 0, 1, 2 or 3 a socket-outlet, other than a SELV socket-outlet or shaver supply unit, must be protected by a residual current device with rated residual operating current ($I_{\Delta n}$) not exceeding 30 mA in accordance with Regulation 412-06.
Note 2: See Figures 5.3a and 5.3b for zones
Note 3: All equipment must be suitable for the zones

▼ **Figure 5.3a** Supplementary bonding in a bathroom – metal pipe installation with soldered joints providing reliable electrical continuity

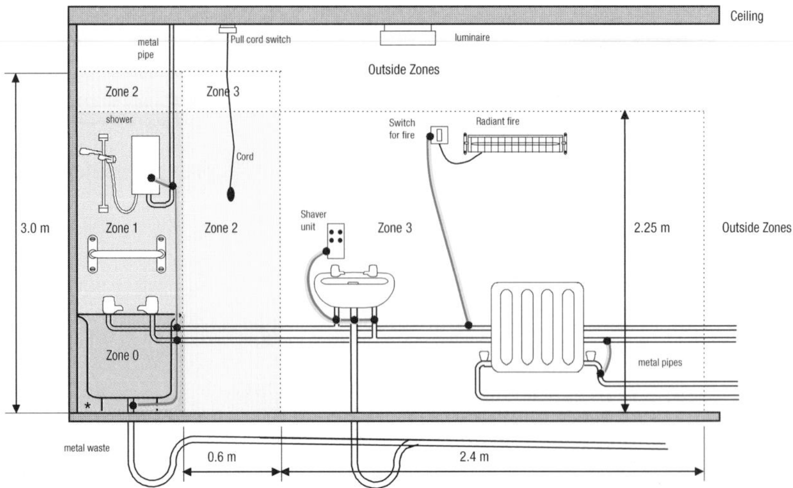

Note 1: The protective conductors of all power and lighting points within the zones must be supplementary bonded to all extraneous-conductive-parts in the zones, including metal waste, water and central heating pipes, and metal baths and metal shower basins.

Note 2: Circuit protective conductors may be used as supplementary bonding conductors.

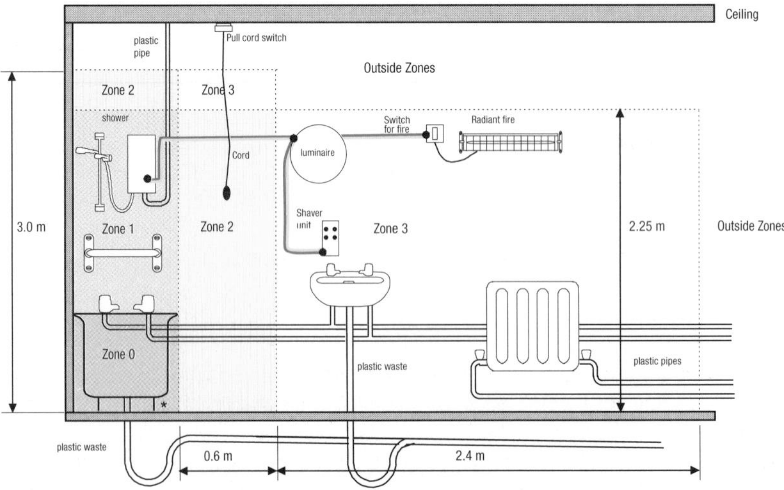

▲ **Figure 5.3b** Supplementary bonding in a bathroom – plastic pipe installation

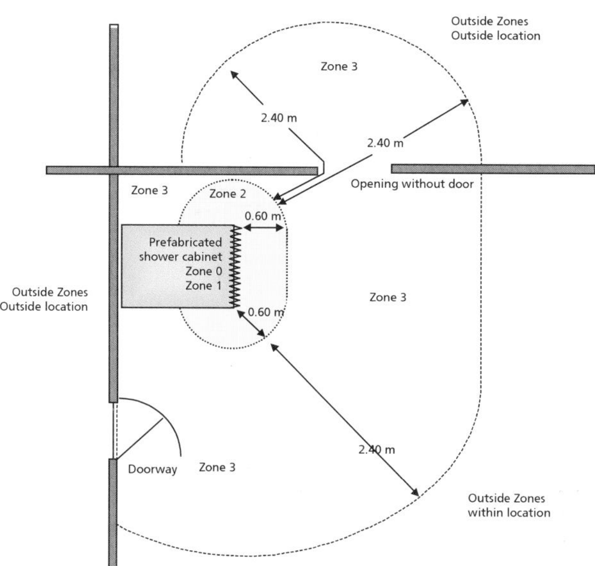

▲ **Figure 5.3c** Plan of zones for equipment in proximity to showers

Plate switches

A plate switch is allowed within zone 3 and outside the zones of a bathroom. A switch should be at least 0.6 metres from the edge of the bath or shower and must be suitable for the location. It is recommended that plate switches be installed outside of zone 3. The cords of cord-operated switches are allowed in zones 1, 2 and 3.

Luminaires (light fittings)

230 V fittings can be installed above a shower or bath but they must be IPX4 i.e. enclosed and water protected unless mounted at a height of more than 3 metres. If installed more than 0.6 metres from the edge of a shower basin or bath, no special fitting is required but the luminaire must be of a suitable design for the conditions.

Shower units

Electric showers and electric shower pumps should comply with BS EN 60335-2-35 and BS EN 60335-2-41 respectively. Such showers are usually suitable for installation within zone 1. Shower circuits are not required by BS 7671 to be protected by an RCD. However, often shower manufacturers in their instructions recommend an RCD be provided. It is normal practice to provide an isolation switch within the bathroom. The switch must be installed outside zones 0, 1 and 2 although the cord of cord operated switches may reach into zones 1 or 2.

Extractor fans

A suitable 230 V extractor fan may be installed in zones 1 and 2 as well as zone 3 and outside the zones. If an extractor fan is installed in zone 1 or 2 it must be protected against the ingress of moisture to at least IPX4. An extractor fan supplied from a lighting circuit for a bathroom without a window should have its own means of isolation, as otherwise replacement or maintenance of the fan would have to be carried out in the dark. An isolation switch for a fan with an overrun facility will need to be triple-pole (switch wire, live, and neutral), and must be installed outside of zones 0, 1 and 2.

Fixed equipment

Fixed equipment that has no protection against ingress of water can be installed in zone 3 and outside the zones of bathrooms including the provision of a switched fused spur providing such equipment is of a suitable design for the conditions.

A supplementary bonding conductor needs to be run to the protective conductor of the circuits supplying the fixed equipment to include the equipment within the supplementary bonding of the bathroom. There is no need for the supplementary bond to be fixed directly to the piece of equipment. The protective conductor in a short flexible cord to fixed equipment is deemed to provide the supplementary bond.

Washing machines and tumble dryers

Washing machines and tumble dryers may be installed in a bathroom provided they are:

- Installed outside zones 0, 1 and 2
- Supplied from a switched fused flex outlet (socket-outlets are not allowed) installed outside zones 0, 1 and 2
- Protected by a 30 mA RCD.
- Permitted for such installation by the manufacturer.

Electric underfloor heating

Underfloor heating installations installed below any of the zones must have an overall earthed metallic grid or the heating cable should have an earthed metallic sheath, which must be connected to the local supplementary equipotential bonding.

5.3.2 Bedrooms with a shower enclosure

The requirements for bathrooms (Section 5.3) are to be met for bedrooms with a shower cubicle except that socket-outlets are allowed in the bedroom provided they are outside of zones 0, 1, 2 or 3 and protected by an RCD. That means that socket-outlets are allowed in bedrooms containing a shower cubicle (unlike bathrooms) providing they are more than 3 metres from the shower cubicle and provided they are protected by an RCD. See Figure 5.3.2.

Supplementary bonding, which is normally required in zones 1, 2 and 3, is only required in zones 1 and 2 where a cabinet containing a shower is installed in a bedroom.

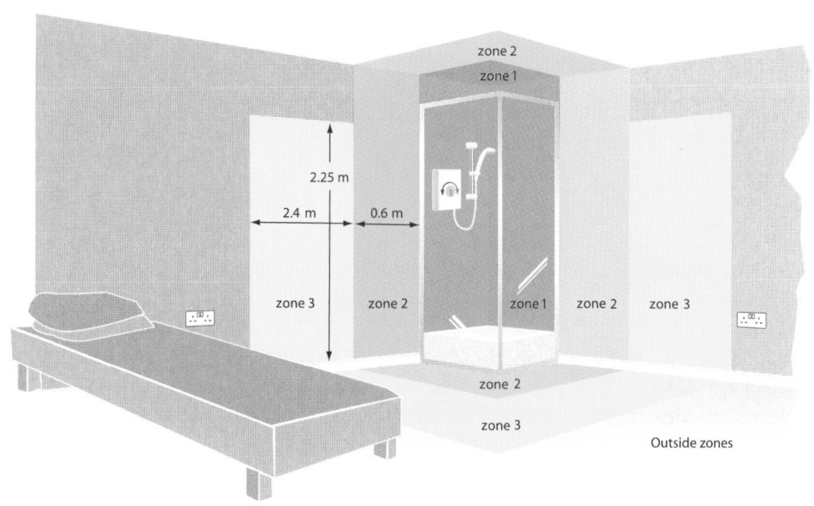

▲ **Figure 5.3.2** Zones in a bedroom with a shower cubicle

5.4 Swimming pools

Persons carrying out electrical installations in swimming pools must be familiar with the requirements of BS 7671, in particular Section 602 and also Guidance Note 7, Chapter 2. This Guide gives advice on the type of precautions that need to be taken.

Summary of the additional supplementary requirements placed by Section 602:

(a) The swimming pool and its surrounding area is divided into three zones, A, B and C (see Figure 5.4).
(b) Local supplementary equipotential bonding is required in all three zones. Where there is a metal grid in the floor, it must be connected to the local supplementary bonding.
(c) With permitted exceptions, in zones A and B the only protective measure against electric shock allowed is SELV at a nominal voltage not exceeding 12 volts a.c. rms or 30 volts d.c.

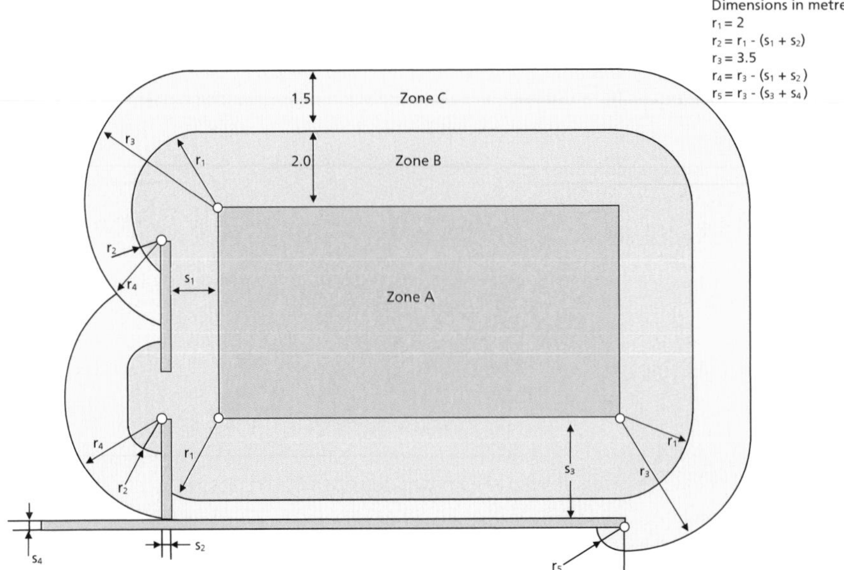

▲ **Figure 5.4** Examples of zone dimensions (plan) with fixed partition height of at least 2.5m

(d) There are particular IP minimum requirements for the zones:

zone A – IPX8 – protection against continuous immersion in water
zone B – IPX5 – protection against water jets. Alternatively IPX4 is acceptable if water jets are not likely to be used for cleaning
zone C – IPX2 – for indoor pools – protection against water dripping
– IPX4 – for outdoor pools – protection against splashing
– IPX5 – where water jets are likely to be used for cleaning.

(e) In zones A and B no surface metal conduit or trunking is allowed nor is the exposed metallic cable sheath of an armoured cable or an exposed earthing conductor.

(f) In zones A and B there should be no switchgear, controlgear, or accessories including socket-outlets, with a permitted exception for socket-outlets in smaller pools.

(g) In zone C socket-outlets are allowed provided they are protected by an RCD and are of an industrial type to BS 4343 or BS EN 60309-2.

Socket-outlets in zone B

The intention is that socket-outlets should not be installed in zone B; however, if a pool and its surrounds are of such a size that it is not possible to install a socket-outlet outside of zone B (which will be necessary for cleaning and similar purposes) a socket-outlet is allowed provided it is either protected by a 30 mA RCD or supplied from a safety isolating transformer and other requirements met – see Section 602 of BS 7671. The socket-outlet will need to be of an industrial type to BS EN 60309-2.

Electricity supply

A distributor may not provide a PME earthing terminal for an installation such as that of a swimming pool. Where, however, a PME earthing terminal is provided, BS 7671 does not preclude its use for an installation which includes a swimming pool, but the installation designer may decide not to employ it because of the possibility of perceived electric shock within the installation or the possible danger from a broken PEN conductor.

Perceived electric shock. A small voltage difference may exist, under normal operating conditions, between the PME earthing terminal at the origin of an installation and 'true' Earth potential. The potential difference is due to the voltage drop in the PEN conductor caused by load current returning to the source of the supply through the PEN conductor which has a certain impedance. The small voltage, above Earth potential could, under certain conditions such as reduced body resistance due to the presence of water, create the possibility of a perceived electric shock for a person simultaneously in contact with a conductive part (for example a handrail which is connected to the supplementary bonding) and 'Earth potential' (for example, an uninsulated, wet, solid floor). Electricity distributors have, in the past, received complaints of perceived electric shock by persons in such locations.

In order to avoid the risk of perceived electric shock, the installation within the location containing a swimming pool may be made part of a TT system. The exposed-conductive-parts and the extraneous-conductive-parts within the location are separated from the PME earthing terminal and the installation in the location is configured to meet all the associated requirements of BS 7671 applicable to a TT system including being connected to earth by a suitable installation earth electrode.

Broken PEN conductor. Under very exceptional circumstances, the supply PEN conductor connection to an installation could be lost due to a failed joint. Where the phase conductor remains unbroken, a risk of electric shock from exposed-conductive-parts and extraneous-conductive-parts could foreseeably arise. In most installations, the main equipotential bonding plays an important role in protecting against the danger from the loss of a PEN conductor.

5.5 Hot air saunas

Introduction

Persons carrying out electrical installations associated with hot air saunas should be familiar with the supplementary requirements of BS 7671 Section 603 and need to make reference to BS 7671 directly and the other guidance such as Guidance Note No 7 or the Commentary. A summary of the supplementary requirements placed by Section 603 is provided below.

Hot air saunas are divided into zones A, B, C and D for the purpose of selecting suitable equipment.

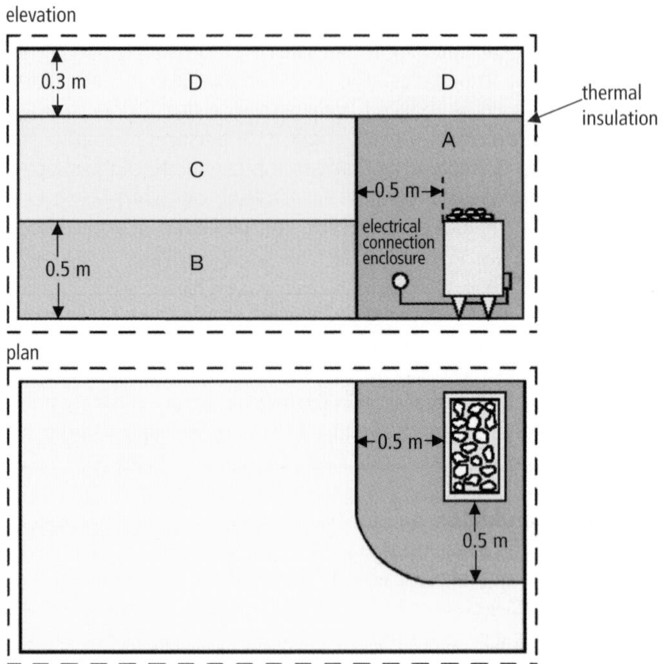

▲ **Figure 5.5** Temperature zones of a hot air sauna

Summary of requirements

- Sauna equipment should meet the requirements of BS EN 60335-2-53 (Electric sauna heating appliances)
- All equipment must have a degree of protection of at least IP24.
- Temperature ratings – equipment in zones C and D must be suitable for an ambient temperature of 125°C.
- In zone D only luminaires and control devices for the sauna heater and associated wiring are allowed.

Wiring
Only flexible cords employing 180°C thermosetting rubber insulation must be used and they are required to be protected against mechanical damage with the materials that meet the requirements for the protection of Class II equipment. (That is reinforced insulation or basic plus supplementary installation.)

Equipment
Only essential equipment should be installed in the sauna i.e. equipment for supplying the sauna heater itself and a luminaire. Wherever possible electrical equipment should be installed outside of the sauna.

Heating elements
The heating elements incorporated in the sauna heater are likely to be metal sheathed. These, unless specified as having waterproof seals, may absorb moisture and cause the operation of the 30 mA RCD if installed. Designers must consult with the equipment suppliers as to whether it is appropriate to install an RCD to protect the installation within the sauna, including the sauna heater.

5.6 Floor and ceiling heating systems

Requirements for floor and ceiling heating systems are outside the scope of this publication.

The risk associated with ceiling heating systems is generally that of penetration of the heating element by nails, pins, etc pushed through the ceiling surface. For this reason, supplementary protection against direct contact is recommended by the use of 30 mA RCDs or the use of electrical separation is recommended.

Similarly for underfloor heating installations there is concern that they could be damaged by carpet gripper rods, nails, etc and, once again, protection by a 30 mA RCD is recommended.

To protect the building structure and to reduce of the risk of fire, there are particular recommendations to avoid overheating of the floor or ceiling heating systems.

Persons installing such systems should obtain specialist advice. Guidance is given in Chapter 14 of Guidance Note 7 – Special Locations.

5.7 Garden lighting and power, sheds and garages

Garden lighting and power, and electrical installations in sheds, garages and greenhouses are within the scope of Part P of the Building Regulations. Furthermore, garden lighting and garden power are not exempt from the minor works relaxation. The addition of a lighting point or socket-outlet to an existing garden lighting or power circuit is notifiable work.

5.7.1 The risk

The general rules for outdoor circuits and equipment apply to all gardens including domestic gardens. Outdoor installations are subject to additional requirements including:

(i) reduced disconnection times for accessible i.e. within arm's reach, fixed Class I equipment
(ii) a socket-outlet rated at 32 A or less is to be additionally protected by a 30 mA RCD
(iii) an item of portable equipment rated at less than 32 A and connected via a flex outlet is also required to be protected by a 30 mA RCD.

5.7.2 Fixed cables

Pvc cables must be protected against direct exposure to sunlight. Cables must be permanently fixed in a protected location or mechanically protected or buried.

Cables buried in the ground have to be buried at a sufficient depth to avoid damage by any disturbance of the ground reasonably likely to occur. As a general rule the minimum depth in all locations should be 500 mm. Double digging is likely to occur in a vegetable plot and if cable is laid in such a location should be at least 600 mm deep.

A buried cable is to be marked by cable covers or a suitable marking tape. It must be remembered that the layout of a garden can be changed and care should be taken to install cables where they are not likely to be damaged or disturbed; such as by laying the cable around the edge of the plot and at sufficient depth. A buried cable route should be identified by a route markers and recorded on drawings retained with the completion certificate. Cables should be buried at least 500 mm, preferably deeper, below the lowest ground level and route marker tape used, laid along the cable route approximately 150 mm below the surface. Armoured cables are generally selected for such installations.

Cables need to be shielded against prolonged exposure to direct sunlight, particularly grey and white pvc cables. Cables with a black or rubber sheath are recommended if direct exposure cannot be avoided. Ultraviolet light from the sun will degrade pvc and unless shielded will need replacing after 15 years. Black pvc and rubber cables have a reasonable life outdoors.

5.7.3 Socket-outlets

Indoor or outdoor socket-outlets that may reasonably be expected to supply portable equipment outdoors must be protected by a 30 mA RCD. Socket-outlets installed out of doors must be of a weatherproof construction (minimum IP54) and must always be protected by a 30 mA RCD.

RCD protection is not required for a circuit at safety extra-low voltage (SELV) or reduced low voltage (RLV).

5.7.4 Fixed equipment

Fixed equipment in the garden, such as permanent lighting attached to buildings, should be securely erected with all cables buried or securely fixed to permanent structures clear of the ground. All insulated Class II equipment is recommended where possible. Outdoor fixed equipment is not required to be protected by an RCD. A reduced disconnection time of 0.4 seconds is required.

5.7.5 Ponds

Ponds are naturally of concern because of the presence of water. All equipment must be specifically designed for pond use and consequently be of a suitable IP rating or installed in a suitable enclosure. Class II equipment is recommended i.e. equipment with an all insulated enclosure. Where practicable, cables should be installed in ducts or conduits built into the pond structure and not left loose on the ground. All electrical connections should be made in robust water-resistant junction boxes having an IP rating of IP 55 or better.

Pond lighting should meet the requirements of BS EN 60598-1, which includes a rating of IPX8 if immersed, otherwise IPX4. Pumps should meet the requirements of BS EN 60335-2-41 and other equipment should meet the requirements of BS EN 60335-2-55.

5.8 Solar photovoltaic systems and small scale embedded generators

The installation of such equipment is outside of the scope of this publication. Guidance is given in IEE Guidance Note 7 – Special Locations.

5.9 Builders supplies

Hand tools including handlamps on any work site including domestic rewires should preferably be supplied from 110 V supplies or protected by a 30 mA RCD.

For installation of supplies to construction sites reference needs to be made to BS 7671 and Guidance Note 7, also HSE publication HS(G) 141 (formerly GS24) Electrical Safety on Construction Sites.

BS 7671 requires 110 V single-phase centre tapped 55 V to earth supplies for portable and hand tools, and lighting up to 2 kW and 110 V three-phase star point earth for small mobile plant up to 3.75 kW.

Inspection and testing

6

- Introduction
- Inspection
- Testing
- Operation of residual current devices

6.1 Introduction

6.1.1 The Building Regulations Part P

Exemptions from requirement to give building notice or deposit full plans (regulation 16A)

Whilst competent persons (firms) registered with a Part P self-certification scheme are exempted from the requirement in the Building Regulations to give building notice they are required to provide a self-certification certificate to the occupier and a notice to that effect (or a copy of the certificate) to the local authority not more than 30 days after completion of the work. Part P requires electrical installations to be inspected and tested as necessary during and on completion of the work and before they are handed over or put into service. The purpose is to verify that the installation complies with Part P and is safe to use.

Precautions must be taken to avoid danger to persons and to avoid damage to property and installed equipment during inspection and testing.

Both Part P and BS 7671 require that as necessary installations may need inspection and testing during the installation work as inspection and testing on completion will not necessarily identify all defects. For example, this is important when cables are concealed.

Part P requires that the installation be Inspected (see Section 6.2), Tested (see Sections 6.3 and 6.4) and supplied:

(a) to the person ordering the work a complete set of forms (completion certificate, schedule of inspections and schedule of tests), signed by a person competent to do so; and
(b) in the case of a competent firm registered with an electrical self-certification scheme, to the Building Control body a declaration that compliance with the Building Regulations has been achieved.

Note: The certificate in (b) may be supplied to Building Control by the self-certification scheme operator on receipt of notification by the competent person/firm.

6.1.2 Forms

Blank forms are available on the IEE website: www.iee.org.uk

When carrying out inspection and testing on an installation, the short form Electrical Installation Certificate (F1) may be used together with Schedule of Inspections (F3) and a Schedule of Test Results (F4).

If other persons including other companies carry out the design and installation, the standard form Electrical Installation Certificate (F2) together with the Schedule of Inspections and Schedule of Test Results is to be used. The signatures of competent persons or firms for design and for construction must be obtained prior to carrying out the inspections and tests.
BS 7671 requires:

(a) The Electrical Installation Certificate must be made out and signed or otherwise authenticated by a competent person or persons in respect of the design, construction, inspection and testing of the work.

(b) A competent person should have a sound knowledge and experience relevant to the nature of the work undertaken, be fully versed in the inspection and testing procedures and employ adequate testing equipment.

(c) Electrical Installation Certificates will indicate the responsibility for design, construction, inspection and testing, whether in relation to new work or further work on an existing installation. Where design, construction and inspection and testing is the responsibility of one person a Certificate with a single signature declaration in the form shown below may replace the multiple signatures section of the model form.

(d) A Schedule of Inspections and a Schedule of Test Results must be issued with the Electrical Installation Certificate.

(e) When making out and signing a form on behalf of a company or other business entity, individuals must state for whom they are acting.

(f) Additional forms or pages may be required to permit explanation. Additional Schedules of Inspection and Schedules of Test Results may be needed for large or more complex installations.

The Electrical Installations Certificates shown overleaf have been completed for typical installations.

Form F1

Form No 123/1

ELECTRICAL INSTALLATION CERTIFICATE (notes 1 and 2)

(REQUIREMENTS FOR ELECTRICAL INSTALLATIONS - BS 7671 [IEE WIRING REGULATIONS])

DETAILS OF THE CLIENT (note 1) House Builder Ltd, 1 City Way, LONDON

INSTALLATION ADDRESS Plot 24, New Road, NEW TOWN, County Postcode AB1 2CD

DESCRIPTION AND EXTENT OF THE INSTALLATION Tick boxes as appropriate

Description of installation: Domestic

Extent of installation covered by this Certificate: Complete electrical, including smoke and intruder alarms

(Use continuation sheet if necessary) see continuation sheet No: ....

New installation ☑

Addition to an existing installation ☐

Alteration to an existing installation ☐

FOR DESIGN, CONSTRUCTION, INSPECTION & TESTING

I being the person responsible for the Design, Construction, Inspection & Testing of the electrical installation (as indicated by my signature below), particulars of which are described above, having exercised reasonable skill and care when carrying out the Design, Construction, Inspection & Testing, hereby CERTIFY that the said work for which I have been responsible is to the best of my knowledge and belief in accordance with BS 7671: 2001, amended to 2004 (date) except for the departures, if any, detailed as follows:

Details of departures from BS 7671 (Regulations 120-01-03, 120-02): None

The extent of liability of the signatory is limited to the work described above as the subject of this Certificate.

Name (IN BLOCK LETTERS): A SMITH Position: Director
Signature (note 3): A Smith Date: 20/4/2005
For and on behalf of: All Electrics Ltd
Address: 27, Central Road, NEW TOWN, County Postcode EF3 4GH Tel No: ....

NEXT INSPECTION

I recommend that this installation is further inspected and tested after an interval of not more than 10 years/~~months~~. (notes 4 and 7)

SUPPLY CHARACTERISTICS AND EARTHING ARRANGEMENTS Tick boxes and enter details, as appropriate

Earthing arrangements	Number and Type of Live Conductors	Nature of Supply Parameters	Supply Protective Device Characteristics
TN-C ☐ TN-S ☐ TN-C-S ☑ TT ☐ IT ☐	a.c. ☑ d.c. ☐ 1-phase, 2-wire ☑ 2-pole ☐ 1-phase, 3-wire ☐ 3-pole ☐ 2-phase, 3-wire ☐ other ☐ 3-phase, 3-wire ☐ 3-phase, 4-wire ☐	Nominal voltage, U/U_o (1) 230 V Nominal frequency, f (1) 50 Hz Prospective fault current, I_{pf} (2) 16 kA (note 6) External loop impedance, Z_e (2) 0.35 Ω (Note: (1) by enquiry, (2) by enquiry or by measurement)	Type: BS 1361 fuse Nominal current rating 100 A
Alternative source of supply (to be detailed on attached schedules) ☐			

Page 1 of 4 (note 5)

▲ Page 1 of the short form electrical installation certificate F1

PARTICULARS OF INSTALLATION REFERRED TO IN THE CERTIFICATE Tick boxes and enter details, as appropriate			
Means of Earthing	**Maximum Demand**		
Distributor's facility ☑	Maximum demand (load) ......60...... Amps per phase		
	Details of Installation Earth Electrode (*where applicable*)		
Installation earth electrode ☐	Type (e.g. rod(s), tape etc) ......None......	Location	Electrode resistance to earth .... Ω
Main Protective Conductors			
Earthing conductor:	material ......Copper.... csa ......16......mm²	connection verified ☑	
Main equipotential bonding conductors	material ......Copper.... csa ......10......mm²	connection verified ☑	
To incoming water and/or gas service ☑	To other elements:		
Main Switch or Circuit-breaker			
BS, Type ..BS EN 60439-3	No. of poles ....2......	Current rating ......80..A	Voltage rating ......230..V
Location ....Garage..........		Fuse rating or setting....——....A	
Rated residual operating current $I_{\Delta n}$ = ...30. mA, and operating time of 200ms (at $I_{\Delta n}$) (applicable only where an RCD is suitable and is used as a main circuit-breaker)			
COMMENTS ON EXISTING INSTALLATION (in the case of an alteration or additions see Section 743):			
........New installation..........			
SCHEDULES (note 2) The attached Schedules are part of this document and this Certificate is valid only when they are attached to it. ....1..... Schedule(s) of Inspections and ...1....... Schedule(s) of Test Results are attached. (Enter quantities of schedules attached).			

Page 2 of 4 (note 5)

▲ Page 2 of the short form electrical installation certificate F1

ELECTRICAL INSTALLATION CERTIFICATES
NOTES FOR SHORT FORM F1 AND STANDARD FORM F2:

1. The Electrical Installation Certificate is to be used only for the initial certification of a new installation or for an alteration or addition to an existing installation where new circuits have been introduced. It is not to be used for a Periodic Inspection for which a Periodic Inspection Report form should be used. For an alteration or addition which does not extend to the introduction of new circuits, a Minor Electrical Installation Works Certificate may be used. The original Certificate is to be given to the person ordering the work (Regulation 742-01-03). A duplicate should be retained by the contractor.
2. This Certificate is only valid if accompanied by the Schedule of Inspections and the Schedule(s) of Test Results.
3. The signatures appended are those of the persons authorised by the companies executing the work of design, construction and inspection and testing respectively. A signatory authorised to certify more than one category of work should sign in each of the appropriate places.
4. The time interval recommended before the first periodic inspection must be inserted (see IEE Guidance Note 3 for guidance).
5. The page numbers for each of the Schedules of Test Results should be indicated, together with the total number of sheets involved.
6. The maximum prospective fault current recorded should be the greater of either the short-circuit current or the earth fault current.
7. The proposed date for the next inspection should take into consideration the frequency and quality of maintenance that the installation can reasonably be expected to receive during its intended life, and the period should be agreed between the designer, installer and other relevant parties.

Form F 2 | Form No 124 /2

ELECTRICAL INSTALLATION CERTIFICATE (notes 1 and 2)
(REQUIREMENTS FOR ELECTRICAL INSTALLATIONS - BS 7671 [IEE WIRING REGULATIONS])

DETAILS OF THE CLIENT (note 1) Adeveloper Ltd, Main Street, London, EF1

INSTALLATION ADDRESS 35 High Street, Town, County Postcode CB1 2ET

DESCRIPTION AND EXTENT OF THE INSTALLATION Tick boxes as appropriate (note 1)

Description of installation: Shop and dwelling

Extent of installation covered by this Certificate: Complete installation

New installation ☑
Addition to an existing installation ☐
Alteration to an existing installation ☐

FOR DESIGN
I/We being the person(s) responsible for the design of the electrical installation (as indicated by my/our signatures below), particulars of which are described above, having exercised reasonable skill and care when carrying out the design hereby CERTIFY that the design work for which I/we have been responsible is to the best of my/our knowledge and belief in accordance with BS 7671 : 2001., amended to 2004 (date) except for the departures, if any, detailed as follows:

Details of departures from BS 7671 (Regulations 120-01-03, 120-02):
None

The extent of liability of the signatory or the signatories is limited to the work described above as the subject of this Certificate.

For the DESIGN of the installation: **(Where there is mutual responsibility for the design)

Signature: B Brown Date: 5/4/2005 Name (BLOCK LETTERS): B BROWN Designer No 1

Signature: — Date: — Name (BLOCK LETTERS): — Designer No 2**

FOR CONSTRUCTION
I/We being the person(s) responsible for the construction of the electrical installation (as indicated by my/our signatures below), particulars of which are described above, having exercised reasonable skill and care when carrying out the construction hereby CERTIFY that the construction work for which I/we have been responsible is to the best of my/our knowledge and belief in accordance with BS 7671 : 2001, amended to 2004 (date) except for the departures, if any, detailed as follows:

Details of departures from BS 7671 (Regulations 120-01-03, 120-02):
None

The extent of liability of the signatory is limited to the work described above as the subject of this Certificate.

For CONSTRUCTION of the installation:
Signature W White Date 6/4/2005
Name (BLOCK LETTERS): W WHITE Constructor

FOR INSPECTION & TESTING
I/We being the person(s) responsible for the inspection & testing of the electrical installation (as indicated by my/our signatures below), particulars of which are described above, having exercised reasonable skill and care when carrying out the inspection & testing hereby CERTIFY that the work for which I/we have been responsible is to the best of my/our knowledge and belief in accordance with BS 7671 : 2001., amended to 2004 (date) except for the departures, if any, detailed as follows:

Details of departures from BS 7671 (Regulations 120-01-03, 120-02):
None

The extent of liability of the signatory is limited to the work described above as the subject of this Certificate.

For INSPECTION AND TEST of the installation:
Signature: S Jones Date: 10/4/2005
Name (BLOCK LETTERS): S JONES Inspector

NEXT INSPECTION (notes 4 and 7)
I/We the designer(s), recommend that this installation is further inspected and tested after an interval of not more than 3 years/~~months~~.

Page 1 of 4

▲ Page 1 of the standard form electrical installation certificate F2

PARTICULARS OF SIGNATORIES TO THE ELECTRICAL INSTALLATION CERTIFICATE

Designer (No 1)
Name: B Brown Company: Design Co Ltd
Address: City Road, Old Town
County Postcode: MP1 2BQ Tel No: 01334/612266

Designer (No 2) (if applicable)
Name: Not applicable Company:
Address:
Postcode: Tel No:

Constructor
Name: W White Company: County Electrics Ltd
Address: 187 Industrial Lane, Town
County Postcode: MP3 8BQ Tel No: 01334/72963

Inspector
Name: S Jones Company: County Electrics Ltd
Address: As above
Postcode: Tel No:

SUPPLY CHARACTERISTICS AND EARTHING ARRANGEMENTS Tick boxes and enter details, as appropriate

Earthing arrangements	Number and Type of Live Conductors	Nature of Supply Parameters	Supply Protective Device Characteristics
TN-C ☐ TN-S ☐ TN-C-S ☑ TT ☐ IT ☐	a.c. ☑ d.c. ☐ 1-phase, 2-wire ☐ 2-pole ☐ 1-phase, 3-wire ☐ 3-pole ☐ 2-phase, 3-wire ☐ other ☐ 3-phase, 3-wire ☐ 3-phase, 4-wire ☑	Nominal voltage, U/U_o (1) 400/230 V Nominal frequency, f (1) 50 Hz (note 6) Prospective fault current, I_{pf} (2) 18 kA External loop impedance, Z_e (2) 0.2 Ω *(Note: (1) by enquiry, (2) by enquiry or by measurement)*	Type: BS 1361 Fuse Nominal current rating 100 A
Alternative source ☐ of supply (to be detailed on attached schedules)			

PARTICULARS OF INSTALLATION REFERRED TO IN THE CERTIFICATE Tick boxes and enter details, as appropriate

Means of Earthing
Distributor's facility ☑
Installation earth electrode ☐

Maximum Demand
Maximum demand (load) 40 Amps per phase

Details of Installation Earth Electrode (*where applicable*)
Type (e.g. rod(s), tape etc): — Location: — Electrode resistance to earth: — Ω

Main Protective Conductors
Earthing conductor: material copper csa 16 mm² connection verified ☑
Main equipotential bonding conductors: material copper csa 10 mm² connection verified ☑
To incoming water and/or gas service ☑ To other elements:

Main Switch or Circuit-breaker
BS, Type BS EN 60947-3 No. of poles 3 Current rating 125 A Voltage rating 400 V
Location Cupboard adjacent to entrance Fuse rating or setting — A
Rated residual operating current $I_{\Delta n}$ = / mA, and operating time of / ms (at $I_{\Delta n}$) (applicable only where an RCD is suitable and is used as a main circuit-breaker)

COMMENTS ON EXISTING INSTALLATION (in the case of an alteration or additions see Section 743):
~~Not applicable~~

SCHEDULES (note 2)
The attached Schedules are part of this document and this Certificate is valid only when they are attached to it.
1 Schedule(s) of Inspections and 1 Schedule(s) of Test Results are attached.
(Enter quantities of schedules attached).

Page 2 of 4

▲ Page 2 of the standard form electrical installation certificate F2

ELECTRICAL INSTALLATION CERTIFICATES
GUIDANCE FOR RECIPIENTS

1. This safety Certificate has been issued to confirm that the electrical installation work to which it relates has been designed, constructed and inspected and tested in accordance with British Standard 7671 (the IEE Wiring Regulations).
2. You should have received an original Certificate and the contractor should have retained a duplicate Certificate. If you were the person ordering the work, but not the user of the installation, you should pass this Certificate, or a full copy of it including the schedules, immediately to the user.
3. The "original" Certificate should be retained in a safe place and be shown to any person inspecting or undertaking further work on the electrical installation in the future. If you later vacate the property, this Certificate will demonstrate to the new owner that the electrical installation complied with the requirements of British Standard 7671 at the time the Certificate was issued. The Construction (Design and Management) Regulations require that for a project covered by those Regulations, a copy of this Certificate, together with schedules, is included in the project health and safety documentation.
4. For safety reasons, the electrical installation will need to be inspected at appropriate intervals by a competent person. The maximum time interval recommended before the next inspection is stated on Page 1 under "Next Inspection".
5. This Certificate is intended to be issued only for a new electrical installation or for new work associated with an alteration or addition to an existing installation. It should not have been issued for the inspection of an existing electrical installation. A "Periodic Inspection Report" should be issued for such a periodic inspection.
6. The Certificate is only valid if a Schedule of Inspections and a Schedule of Test Results is appended.

6.2 Inspection

6.2.1 General

Every installation must be inspected (and tested) during erection as necessary and on completion and before being put into service to provide a visual check that the installation including the installed equipment complies with the requirements of BS 7671.

The inspection will check that equipment is:

(i) made in compliance with appropriate British Standards or European Standards;
(ii) selected and installed in accordance with BS 7671 (including consideration of external influences such as the presence of moisture);
(iii) not visibly damaged or defective so as to be unsafe.

Inspection must precede testing and is normally to be done with that part of the installation under inspection disconnected from the supply.

Defects or omissions revealed during inspection of the installation work covered by the Schedule of Inspection (F3) must be made good before the Electrical Installations Certificate is issued. If the inspection reveals no departures it must be signed in preparation for giving to the person ordering the work as part of the set of forms.

A sample Form F3 overleaf has been completed for a typical domestic dwelling. Blank forms are available on the IEE website.

Form F3 | Form No 123/3

SCHEDULE OF INSPECTIONS

Methods of protection against electric shock

(a) Protection against both direct and indirect contact:

- N/A (i) SELV (note 1)
- N/A (ii) Limitation of discharge of energy (note 2)

(b) Protection against direct contact: (note 3)

- ✓ (i) Insulation of live parts
- ✓ (ii) Barriers or enclosures
- N/A (iii) Obstacles (note 4)
- N/A (iv) Placing out of reach (note 5)
- N/A (v) PELV (note 6)
- ✓ (vi) Presence of RCD for supplementary protection

(c) Protection against indirect contact:

(i) EEBAD (note 7) including:

- ✓ Presence of earthing conductor
- ✓ Presence of circuit protective conductors
- ✓ Presence of main equipotential bonding conductors
- ✓ Presence of supplementary equipotential bonding conductors
- N/A Presence of earthing arrangements for combined protective and functional purposes (note 8)
- N/A Presence of adequate arrangements for alternative source(s), where applicable
- ✓ Presence of residual current device(s)

- N/A (ii) Use of Class II equipment or equivalent insulation (note 9)
- N/A (iii) Non-conducting location: (note 10) Absence of protective conductors
- N/A (iv) Earth-free equipotential bonding: (note 11) Presence of earth-free equipotential bonding conductors
- N/A (v) Electrical separation (note 12)

Prevention of mutual detrimental influence

- ✓ (a) Proximity of non-electrical services and other influences
- ✓ (b) Segregation of band I and band II circuits or band II insulation used
- ✓ (c) Segregation of safety circuits

Identification

- ✓ (a) Presence of diagrams, instructions, circuit charts and similar information
- ✓ (b) Presence of danger notices and other warning notices
- ✓ (c) Labelling of protective devices, switches and terminals
- ✓ (d) Identification of conductors

Cables and conductors

- ✓ (a) Routing of cables in prescribed zones or within mechanical protection
- ✓ (b) Connection of conductors
- ✓ (c) Erection methods
- ✓ (d) Selection of conductors for current-carrying capacity and voltage drop
- ✓ (e) Presence of fire barriers, suitable seals and protection against thermal effects

General

- ✓ (a) Presence and correct location of appropriate devices for isolation and switching
- ✓ (b) Adequacy of access to switchgear and other equipment
- ✓ (c) Particular protective measures for special installations and locations
- ✓ (d) Connection of single-pole devices for protection or switching in phase conductors only
- ✓ (e) Correct connection of accessories and equipment
- N/A (f) Presence of undervoltage protective devices
- ✓ (g) Choice and setting of protective and monitoring devices for protection against indirect contact and/or overcurrent
- ✓ (h) Selection of equipment and protective measures appropriate to external influences
- ✓ (i) Selection of appropriate functional switching devices

Inspected by ...A. Smith..................... Date ....20/4/2005...........................

Notes:

✓ to indicate an inspection has been carried out and the result is satisfactory

✗ to indicate an inspection has been carried out and the result was unsatisfactory

N/A to indicate the inspection is not applicable

LIM to indicate that, exceptionally, a limitation agreed with the person ordering the work prevented the inspection or test being carried out.

1. SELV An extra-low voltage system which is electrically separate from earth and from other systems. The particular requirements of the Regulations must be checked (see Regulations 411-02 and 471-02)
2. Limitation of discharge of energy - not adopted for domestic installations, used on appliances and equipment.
3. Method of protection against direct contact - will include measurement of distances where appropriate.
4. Obstacles - not suitable for domestic installations, only adopted in special circumstances (see Regulations 412-04 and 471-06)
5. Placing out of reach - not suitable for domestic installations, only adopted in special circumstances (see Regulations 412-05 and 471-07)
6. PELV An extra-low voltage system which is electrically separate from other systems but not earth. The particular requirements of the Regulations must be checked (see Regulations 411-02 and 471-14)
7. EEBAD Earthed equipotential bonding and automatic disconnection of supply, the common form of indirect shock protection
8. Combined protective and functional earthing - it is normal to combine protective and functional earthing. In non-domestic systems functional earthing of IT systems may be separated, (clean earth).
9. Use of Class II equipment - not suitable for domestic installations, infrequently adopted and only when the installation is to be supervised (see Regulations 413-03 and 471-09)
10. Non-conducting locations - not suitable for domestic installations and requiring special precautions (see Regulations 413-04 and 471-10)
11. Earth-free local equipotential bonding - not suitable for domestic installations, only used in special circumstances (see Regulations 413-05 and 471-14)
12. Electrical separation - not adopted in domestic installations (see Regulations 413-06 and 471-12)

Page 3 of 4

▲ Page 3, schedule of inspections F3 of either the short form or standard form electrical installation certificates

6.3 Testing

6.3.1 Safety and equipment

(i) Electrical testing involves a degree of risk. The tester is responsible not only for his or her own safety, but also for the safety of others.

(ii) When design and construction have been carried out by others, a standard form F2 signed by the competent persons responsible for design and construction should be in the possession of the inspector before starting inspection and testing.

(iii) Inspection always precedes testing.

(iv) Dead tests always precede live tests.

(v) On each occasion before using test equipment the tester must confirm that all leads, probes, accessories (including all devices such as crocodile clips used to attach conductors) and instruments are undamaged and are functional.

(vi) Manufacturers' instructions must be read before using equipment and followed. It should be noted that some test instrument manufacturers advise that their instruments be used in conjunction with fused test leads and probes.

6.3.2 Schedule of test results

The schedule of test results must be recorded during testing, must identify every circuit, including its related protective device(s), and must record the results of the appropriate tests and measurements.

(The Schedule is also reproduced overleaf.)

Form 4 — Form No 123 /4

SCHEDULE OF TEST RESULTS

Contractor: ~~All Electrics Ltd~~
Test Date: 20/4/2005
Signature: *A Smith*

Address/Location of distribution board: Plot 24, New Road, Town, County

* Type of Supply: ~~TN-S~~/TN-C-S/~~TT~~
* Ze at origin: 0.35 ohms
* PFC: 16 kA

Instruments
loop impedance: AB11
continuity: AB 22
insulation: AB 44
RCD tester: AB55

Method of protection against indirect contact: E. E. B. A. D. S.

Equipment vulnerable to testing: ~~30 mA RCDs circuits 7 and 4, dimmer and fluorescent circuit 2, Shower circuit 6~~

Description of Work: House electrical installation

Circuit Description	Overcurrent Device (* Short-circuit capacity: 6 kA) type	Rating I_n A	Wiring Conductors live mm²	cpc mm²	Continuity $R_1 + R_2$ Ω	R_2 Ω	Ring	Insulation Resistance Live/Live MΩ	Live/Earth MΩ	Polarity	Earth Loop Impedance Z_s Ω	Functional Testing RCD time ms	Other	Remarks
1	2	3	4	5	*6	*7	*8	*9	*10	*11	*12	*13	*14	15
1 Lights up	B	10	1.5	1.0	2.4	—	—	50	40	✓	2.8	—	✓	
2 Lights down	B	10	1.5	1.0	2.7	—	—	—	30	✓	3.1	—	✓	Dimmer
3 Sockets up	B	32	2.5	1.5	0.4	0.3	✓	30	30	✓	0.8	—	✓	
4 Sockets down	B	32	2.5	1.5	0.5	0.3	✓	—	30	✓	0.9	200	✓	RCD, Vulnerable
5 Cooker	B	32	6.0	2.5	0.1	—	—	50	40	✓	0.5	—	✓	
6 Shower	B	45	10.0	4.0	0.15	—	—	—	40	✓	0.5	200	✓	Electronic
7 Garage	B	20	2.5	1.5	0.4	—	—	—	30	✓	0.8	200	✓	RCD

Deviations from Wiring Regulations and special notes:

None

* See notes on schedule of test results

Page 4 of 4

▲ Page 4, schedule of test results F4 of either the short form or standard form electrical installation certificates

Form 4

Form No 123 /4

SCHEDULE OF TEST RESULTS

Contractor: All Electrics Ltd

Test Date: 20/4/2005

Signature: *A Smith*

Address/Location of distribution board: Plot 24, New Road, Town, County

* Type of Supply: ~~TN-S~~/TN-C-S/~~TT~~

* Ze at origin: 0.35 ohms

* PFC: 16 kA

Instruments

loop impedance: AB11

continuity: AB 22

insulation: AB 44

RCD tester: AB55

Method of protection against indirect contact: E. E. B. A. D. S.

Equipment vulnerable to testing: 30 mA RCDs circuits 7 and 4, dimmer and fluorescent circuit 2, Shower circuit 6

Description of Work: House electrical installation

Circuit Description	Overcurrent Device * Short-circuit capacity: 6 kA		Wiring Conductors		Test Results: Continuity			Insulation Resistance		Polarity	Earth Loop Impedance Z_s	Functional Testing		Remarks
	type	Rating I_n A	live mm²	cpc mm²	$R_1 + R_2$ Ω	R_2 Ω	Ring	Live/Live MΩ	Live/Earth MΩ		Ω	RCD time ms	Other	
1	2	3	4	5	* 6	* 7	* 8	* 9	* 10	* 11	* 12	* 13	* 14	15
1 Lights up	B	10	1.5	1.0	2.4	—	—	50	40	✓	2.8	—	✓	
2 Lights down	B	10	1.5	1.0	2.7	—	—	—	30	✓	3.1	—	✓	Dimmer
3 Sockets up	B	32	2.5	1.5	0.4	0.3	✓	30	30	✓	0.8	—	✓	
4 Sockets down	B	32	2.5	1.5	0.5	0.3	✓	—	30	✓	0.9	200	✓	RCD, Vulnerable
5 Cooker	B	32	6.0	2.5	0.1	—	—	50	40	✓	0.5	—	✓	
6 Shower	B	45	10.0	4.0	0.15	—	—	—	40	✓	0.5	200	✓	Electronic
7 Garage	B	20	2.5	1.5	0.4	—	—	—	30	✓	0.8	200	✓	RCD

Deviations from Wiring Regulations and special notes:

None

* See notes on schedule of test results

Page 4 of 4

NOTES ON THE SCHEDULE OF TEST RESULTS

***Type of supply** is ascertained from the distributor or by inspection.

***Ze at origin.** Preferably the maximum value declared by the distributor is inserted. For PME (TN-C-S) domestic single phase supplies the value will not exceed 0.35 Ω. The effectiveness of the earth must be confirmed by a test. If measured the main bonding will need to be disconnected for the duration of the test.

***Short-circuit capacity** of the protective device is noted.
Consumer units including protective devices complying as a whole assembly with BS EN 60439-3 (Including Annex ZA) or BS 5486-13 are suitable for locations with fault currents up to 16 kA when supplied through a type II fuse to BS 1361 : 1971 (1992) rated at no more than 100 A. Otherwise see Table 7.2A of the On-Site Guide or 2.7.15 of GN3.

***Prospective fault current (pfc).** The value recorded is the greater of either the short-circuit current or the earth fault current. Preferably determined by enquiry from the distributor. For domestic supplies, except for London and some other major city centres, the maximum fault current for 230 V single-phase supplies up to 100 A will not exceed 16 kA.

The following tests, where relevant, must be carried out in the following sequence:

Continuity of protective conductors, including main and supplementary bonding.

Every protective conductor, including main and supplementary bonding conductors, should be tested to verify that they are continuous and correctly connected.

Column 6 Continuity
Where Test Method 1 is used, enter the measured resistance of the phase conductor plus the circuit protective conductor (R_1+ R_2). See 6.3.4 or 10.3.1 of the On-Site Guide or 2.7.5 of GN3.

During the continuity testing (Test Method 1) the following polarity checks are to be carried out:

(a) Every fuse and single-pole control and protective device is connected in the phase conductor only
(b) Centre-contact bayonet and Edison screw lampholders have the outer contact connected to the neutral conductor
(c) Wiring is correctly connected to socket-outlets and similar accessories.

Compliance is to be indicated by a tick in polarity column 11.
(R_1 + R_2) need not be recorded if R_2 is recorded in column 7.

Column 7 Where Test Method 2 is used, the maximum value of R_2 is recorded in column 7.
Where the alternative method of Regulation 413-02-12 is used for shock protection, the resistance of the circuit protective conductor R_2 is measured and recorded in column 7.
See 6.3.4 or 10.3.1 of the On-Site Guide or 2.7.5 of GN3.

Column 8 Continuity of ring final conductors
A test shall be made to verify the continuity of each conductor including the protective conductor of every ring final circuit.

See 6.3.5 or 10.3.2 of the On-Site Guide or 2.7.6 of GN3.

Columns 9 and 10 Insulation Resistance
All voltage sensitive devices to be disconnected or test between live conductors (phase and neutral) connected together and earth.

The insulation resistance between live conductors is to be inserted in column 9.

The minimum insulation resistance values are given in Table 10.1 of the On-Site Guide or Table 2.2 of GN3.

See 6.3.6 or 10.3.3(iv) of the On-Site Guide or 2.7.7 of GN3.

All the preceding tests should be carried out before the installation is energised.

Column 11 Polarity
A satisfactory polarity test should be indicated by a tick in column 11.

Only in a Schedule of Test Results associated with a Periodic Inspection Report is it acceptable to record incorrect polarity.

Column 12 Earth fault loop impedance Zs
This may be determined either by direct measurement at the furthest point of a live circuit or by adding (R_1 + R_2) of column 6 to Ze. Ze is determined by measurement at the origin of the installation or preferably the value declared by the distributor used. $Z_s = Z_e + (R_1 + R_2)$. Zs should be less than the values given in the circuit tables in Chapter 4 or Appendix 2 of the On-Site Guide or Appendix 2 of GN3.

Column 13 Functional testing
The operation of RCDs (including RCBOs) shall be tested by simulating a fault condition, independent of any test facility in the device.

Record operating time in column 13. Effectiveness of the test button must be confirmed. See 6.4 or Section 11 of the On-Site Guide or 2.7.16 of GN3.

Column 14 All switchgear and controlgear assemblies, drives, control and interlocks, etc must be operated to ensure that they are properly mounted, adjusted, and installed.

Satisfactory operation is indicated by a tick in column 14.

Earth electrode resistance
The earth electrode resistance of TT installations must be measured, and normally an RCD is required.

For reliability in service the resistance of any earth electrode should be below 200 Ω. Record the value on Forms 1, 2 or 6 as appropriate. See 6.3.8 or 10.3.5 of the On-Site Guide or 2.7.13 of GN3.

6.3.3 Sequence of tests

Tests should be carried out in the following sequence:

Before the supply is connected
(i) continuity of protective conductors, including main and supplementary bonding
(ii) continuity of ring final circuit conductors, including protective conductors
(iii) insulation resistance
(iv) polarity (by continuity methods)
(v) earth electrode resistance, when using an earth electrode resistance tester (see also vii).

With the supply connected
(vi) re-check of polarity
(vii) earth electrode resistance, when using a loop impedance tester
(viii) earth fault loop impedance
(ix) prospective fault current measurement, if not determined by enquiry of the distributor
(x) functional testing.

Results obtained during tests should be recorded in the Schedule of Test Results.

6.3.4 Continuity of protective and bonding conductors

(For ring final circuits see 6.3.5.)

Every protective conductor including the earthing conductor and main and supplementary equipotential bonding conductors should be tested to verify that the conductors are electrically sound and correctly connected.

Test Method 1 is suitable for testing the continuity of circuit protective conductors. Test Method 2 is suitable for testing the continuity of earthing and bonding conductors and circuit protective conductors.

Test method 1 (for circuit protective conductors)
Test Method 1, detailed below, as well as checking the continuity of the protective conductor, also measures ($R_1 + R_2$) which, when added to the external impedance (Ze), enables the earth-fault loop impedance (Zs) to be checked against the design value, see Section 6.3.9. Note: ($R_1 + R_2$) is the sum of the resistances of the phase conductor (R_1) and the circuit protective conductor (R_2) between the point of utilisation and the origin of the installation.

Use an ohmmeter capable of measuring a low resistance for these tests.

Test Method 1 can only be used to measure ($R_1 + R_2$) for an 'all insulated' installation. Installations incorporating steel conduit, steel trunking, micc and pvc/swa cables will produce parallel paths to protective conductors. Such installations should be inspected for soundness of construction and Test Method 1 or 2 used to prove continuity.

▼ **Fig 6.3.4** Connections for testing continuity of protective conductors. Test Method 1

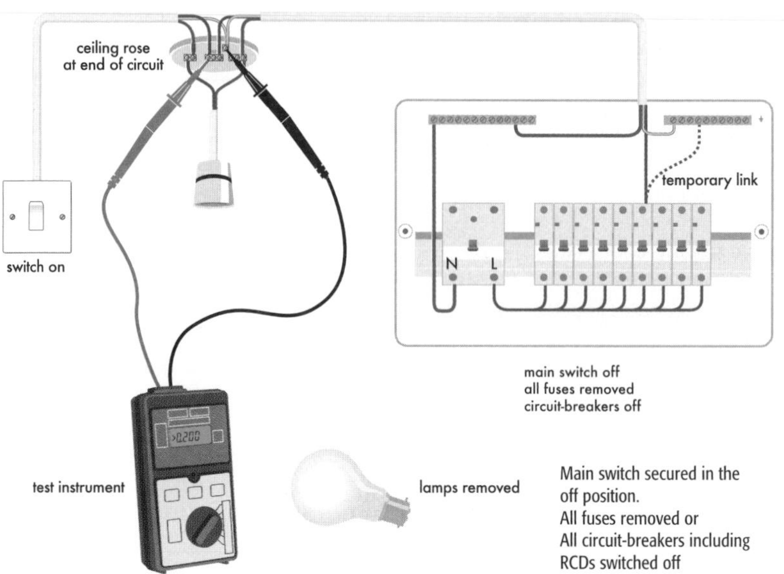

Test method 1 procedure

If the instrument does not include an "auto-null" facility, or this is not used, the resistance of the test leads should be measured and deducted from the resistance readings obtained.

Bridge the phase conductor to the circuit protective conductor at the consumer unit or distribution board so as to include all the circuit. Then test between phase and earth terminals at each point in the circuit.

The measurement at the circuit's extremity should be recorded on the schedule of test results F4 and is the value of (R_1 + R_2) for the circuit under test (see Fig 6.3.4).

Test method 2

Test method 2 may be used for checking the continuity of all protective conductors including earthing and bonding conductors. The method measures R_2 only.

Test method 2 procedure

Connect one terminal of the continuity test instrument to a long test lead and connect this to the consumer's main earthing terminal. Connect the other terminal of the instrument to another test lead and use this to make contact with the protective conductor at various points on the circuit, such as luminaires, switches, spur outlets etc. The resistance of the protective conductor R_2 is recorded on the Schedule of Test Results, Form F4.

6.3.5 Continuity of ring final circuit conductors

For each ring final circuit a three step test is required to verify the continuity of the phase, neutral and protective conductors and correct wiring of every ring final circuit. The test results show if the ring has been correctly connected in an unbroken loop without interconnections.

Step 1:

The phase, neutral and protective conductors are identified at the distribution board or consumer unit and the end-to-end resistance of each is measured separately (see Fig 6.3.5a). These resistances are r_1, r_n and r_2 respectively. A finite reading confirms that there is no open circuit on the ring conductors under test. The resistance values obtained should be the same (within 0.05 ohm) if the conductors are the same size. If the protective

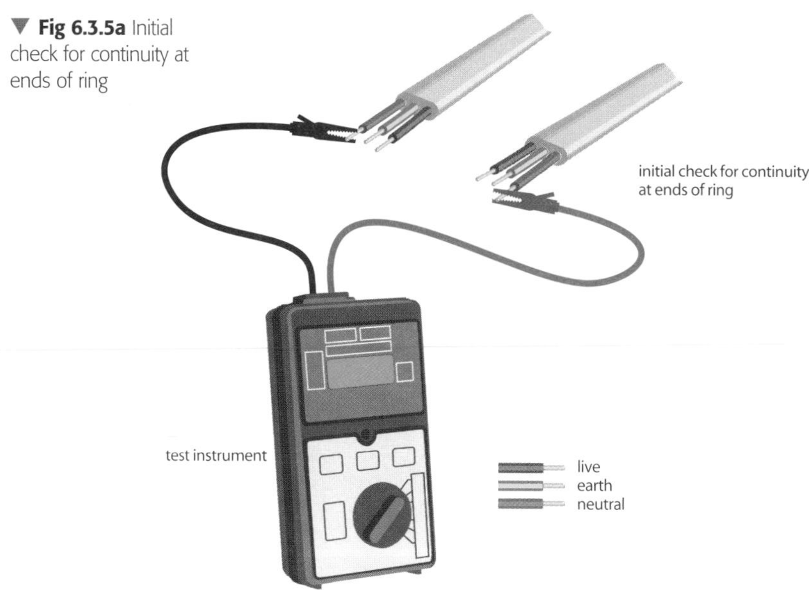

▼ **Fig 6.3.5a** Initial check for continuity at ends of ring

conductor has a reduced csa the resistance r_2 of the protective conductor loop will be proportionally higher than that of the phase and neutral loops e.g. 1.67 times for 2.5/1.5 mm² cable. If these relationships are not achieved then either the conductors are incorrectly identified or there is something wrong at one or more of the accessories.

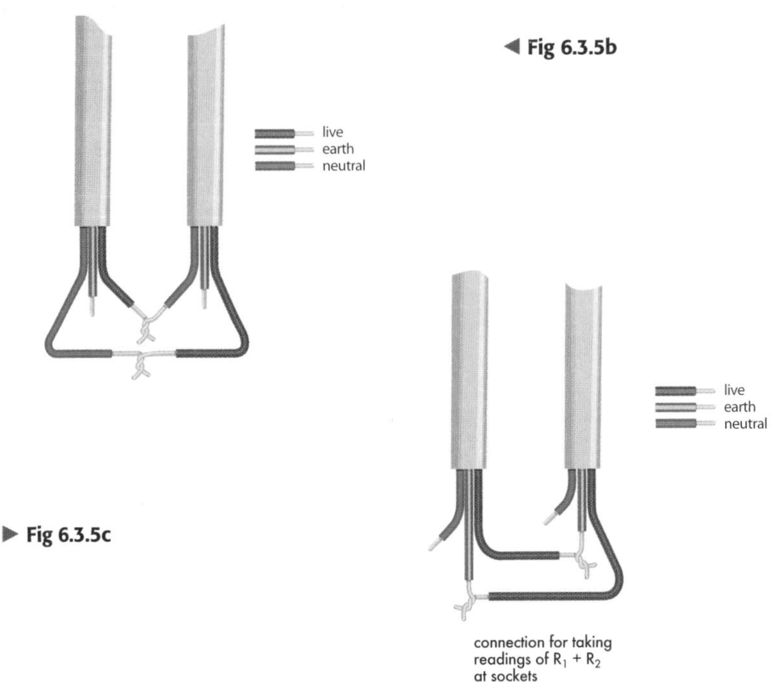

◀ **Fig 6.3.5b**

▶ **Fig 6.3.5c**

Step 2:

The phase and neutral conductors are then connected together so that the outgoing phase conductor is connected to the returning neutral conductor and vice-versa (see Fig 6.3.5b). The resistance between phase and neutral conductors is measured at each socket-outlet. The readings at each of the socket-outlets wired into the ring will be substantially the same and the value will be approximately one quarter of the resistance of the phase plus the neutral loop resistances, i.e. $(r_1 + r_n)/4$. Any socket-outlets wired as spurs will have a higher resistance value due to the resistance of the spur conductors.

Note: Where single-core cables are used, care should be taken to verify that the phase and neutral conductors of opposite ends of the ring circuit are connected together. An error in this respect will be apparent from the readings taken at the socket-outlets. The reading will progressively increase in value as readings are taken towards the midpoint of the ring, then decrease again towards the other end of the ring.

Step 3:
The above step is then repeated, this time with the phase and cpc cross-connected (see Fig 6.3.5c). The resistance between phase and earth is measured at each socket-outlet. The readings obtained at each of the socket-outlets wired into the ring will be substantially the same and the value will be approximately one quarter of the resistance of the phase plus cpc loop resistances, i.e. $(r_1+r_2)/4$. As before, a higher resistance value will be recorded at any socket-outlet wired as a spur. The highest value recorded represents the maximum $(R_1 + R_2)$ of the circuit and is recorded on the Schedule and Test Results. The value can be used to determine the earth loop impedance (Zs) of the circuit to verify compliance with the loop impedance requirements of BS 7671 (see the Circuit Tables in Chapter 4).

This sequence of tests also verifies the polarity at each socket-outlet and accessory unless the testing has been carried out at the terminals on the reverse of the socket-outlet. In such cases, a visual inspection is required to confirm correct polarity connections, at the socket-outlet and accessory and dispenses with the need for a separate polarity test.

6.3.6 Insulation resistance

Pre-test

(a) Check pilot or indicator lamps, and capacitors are disconnected from circuits to avoid misleading test values being obtained.

(b) If a circuit includes voltage-sensitive electronic devices such as dimmer switches, touch switches, delay timers, power controllers, electronic starters, controlgear for fluorescent lamps or RCDs with electronic amplifiers etc either:

- the devices must be temporarily disconnected, or
- measurements should only be made between live conductors (phase and neutral) connected together and the protective earth.

(c) Tests should be carried out using the appropriate d.c. test voltage specified in Table 6.3.6.

(d) The tests should be made at each consumer unit or distribution board with the main switch off, all fuses in place, switches and circuit-breakers closed, lamps removed and other current-using equipment disconnected. Earthing and equipotential bonding conductors are connected.

(e) Where the removal of lamps and/or the disconnection of current-using equipment is impracticable, the local switches controlling such lamps and/or equipment should be open.

(f) Where any circuits contain two-way switching the two-way switches must be operated one at a time and further insulation resistance tests carried out to ensure that all the circuit wiring is tested.

Although an insulation resistance value of not less than 0.5 megohm complies with BS 7671, where an insulation resistance of less than 2 megohms is recorded the possibility of a latent defect exists, which should be investigated.

Where electronic devices are disconnected for the purpose of the tests on the installation wiring (and the devices have exposed-conductive-parts required by BS 7671 to be connected to the protective conductors) the insulation resistance between the exposed-conductive-parts and all live parts of the device (phase and neutral connected together) should be measured separately and should not be less than the values stated in Table 6.3.6.

Table 6.3.6 Minimum values of insulation resistance

Circuit nominal voltage	Test voltage (V d.c.)	Minimum insulation resistance (M ohms)
SELV and PELV	250	0.25
Up to and including 500 V with the exception of SELV and PELV, but including FELV	500	0.5

Insulation resistance between live conductors
Single-phase and three-phase
Test between all the live (phase and neutral) conductors at the distribution board (see Fig 6.3.6a).

Resistance readings obtained should be not less than the minimum values referred to in Table 6.3.6.

Insulation resistance to earth
Single-phase
Test between the live conductors (phase and neutral) and the circuit protective conductors at the distribution board (see Fig 6.3.6b).

For circuits containing two-way switching or two-way and intermediate switching the switches must be operated one at a time and the circuit subjected to additional insulation resistance tests.

Three-phase
Test to Earth from all live conductors (including the neutral) connected together. Where a low reading is obtained it is necessary to test each conductor separately to earth, after disconnecting all equipment.

Resistance readings obtained should be not less than the minimum values referred to in Table 6.3.6.

▼ **Fig 6.3.6a** Insulation resistance tests between live conductors of a circuit

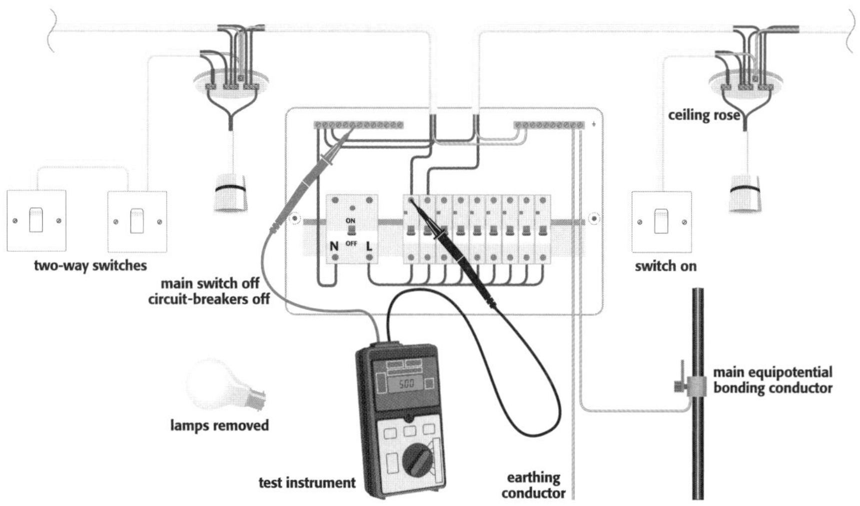

Note: the test should initially be carried out on the complete installation

▼ **Fig 6.3.6b** Insulation resistance tests to earth

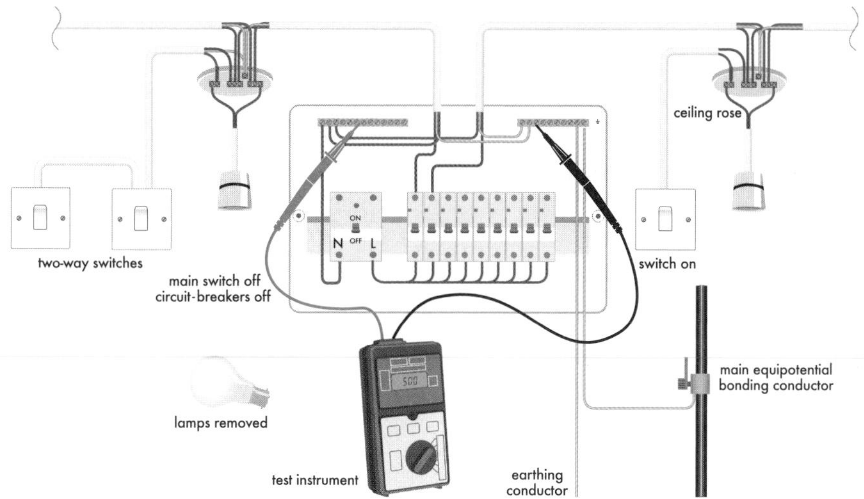

Note 1: the test should initially be carried out on the complete installation
Note 2: bonding and earthing connections are connected

SELV and PELV circuits

Test between SELV and PELV circuits and live parts of other circuits at 500 V d.c.
Test between SELV or PELV conductors at 250 V d.c. and between PELV conductors and protective conductors of the PELV circuit at 250 V d.c.

FELV circuits

FELV circuits are tested as LV circuits at 500 V d.c.

6.3.7 Polarity

See Figure 6.3.7.

The method of test prior to connecting the supply is the same as Test Method 1 for checking the continuity of protective conductors which should have already been carried out (see Section 6.3.4 and Figures 6.3.4 and 6.3.5). For ring final circuits a visual check may be required (see 6.3.5 following step 3).

It is important to confirm that:

(i) overcurrent devices and single-pole controls are connected in the phase conductor
(ii) except for E14 and E27 lampholders to BS EN 60238, centre contact screw lampholders have the outer threaded contact connected to the neutral and
(iii) socket-outlet polarities are correct.

▼ **Fig 6.3.7** Polarity test on a lighting circuit

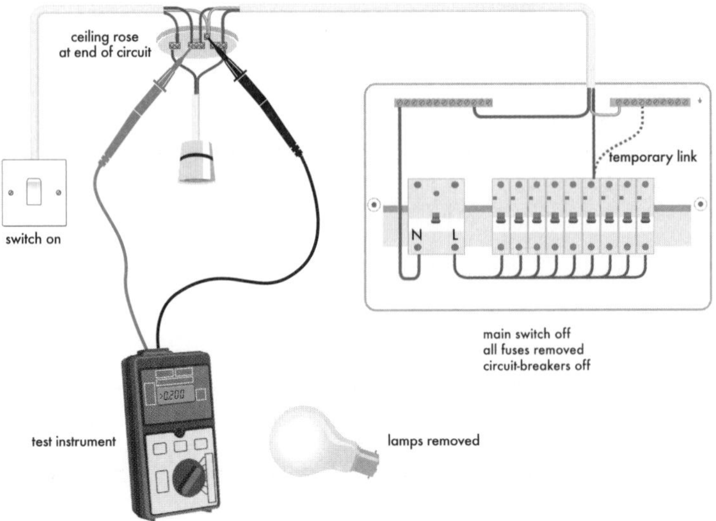

Note: the polarity of E14 and E27 Edison screw lamp holders to BS EN 60238 does not have to be verified.

After connection of the supply polarity must be checked using a voltmeter or a test lamp (with fused leads if advised by the manufacturer).

6.3.8 Earth electrode resistance

If the electrode under test is being used in conjunction with an RCD protecting an installation, the following method of test may be applied.

A loop impedance tester is connected between the phase conductor at the origin of the installation and the earth electrode with the test link open, and a test performed. This impedance reading is treated as the electrode resistance and is then added to the resistance of the protective conductor for the protected circuits. The test should be carried out before energising the remainder of the installation.

The measured resistance should meet the following criteria and those of 6.3.9 but in any case should not exceed 200 ohms.

For TT systems, the value of the earth electrode resistance R_A in ohms multiplied by the operating current in amperes of the protective device $I_{\Delta n}$ must not exceed 50 V e.g. if $R_A = 200\ \Omega$, then the maximum RCD operating current should not exceed 250 mA.

Remember to replace the test link.

6.3.9 Earth fault loop impedance

The earth fault loop impedance (Zs) is required to be determined for the furthest point of each circuit. It may be determined:

- by direct measurement of Zs
- by direct measurement of Ze at the origin and adding $(R_1 + R_2)$ measured during the continuity tests (6.3.4 and 6.3.5) $(Zs = Ze + (R_1 + R_2))$
- by adding $(R_1 + R_2)$ measured during the continuity tests to the value of Ze declared by the distributor (see Chapter 3, e.g. 0.35 ohms for PME). The effectiveness of the distributor's earth must be confirmed by a test.

The external impedance (Ze) may be measured using a phase-earth loop impedance tester.

The main switch is opened and made secure to disconnect the installation from the source of supply. The earthing conductor is disconnected from the Main Earthing Terminal and the measurement made between phase and earth of the supply.

Remember to reconnect the earthing conductor to the earth terminal after the tests.

Direct measurement of Zs can only be made on a live installation. Neither the connection with Earth nor bonding conductors are disconnected. The reading given by the loop impedance tester will usually be less than Ze + (R_1 + R_2) because of parallel earth return paths provided by any bonded extraneous-conductive-parts. This must be taken into account when comparing the results with design data.

Care should be taken to avoid any shock hazard to the testing personnel and to other persons on site during the tests.

The values of Zs determined should be less than the value given in the standard circuit schedules in Chapter 4 for the particular circuit, overcurrent device and cable.

For TN systems, when protection is afforded by an RCD, the rated residual operating current in amperes times the earth fault loop impedance in ohms should not exceed 50 V. This test should be carried out before energising other parts of the system.

Note: For further information on the measurement of earth fault loop impedance, refer to Guidance Note No 3 – Inspection and Testing.

6.3.10 Measurement of prospective fault current

It is not recommended that installation designs are based on measured values of prospective fault current, as changes to the distribution network subsequent to the completion of the installation may increase fault levels.

Designs should be based on the maximum fault current provided by the distributor for a domestic premise, normally a conditional rating of 16 kA (see Chapter 3 and notes in 6.3.2).

If it is desired to measure prospective fault levels this should be done with all main bonding in place. Measurements are made at the distribution board between live conductors and between phase conductors and earth.

For three-phase supplies the maximum possible fault level will be approximately twice the single-phase to neutral value.

6.3.11 Functional testing

RCDs should be tested as described in Section 6.4. All assemblies including switchgear, controls, and interlocks should be functionally tested; that is, operated to check that they work and are properly fixed etc.

6.4. Operation of residual current devices (RCDs) and residual current breakers with overcurrent protection (RCBOs)

6.4.1 Test procedure

Where a residual current device (RCD) provides protection against indirect contact or supplementary protection against direct contact, its effectiveness must be verified by a test simulating an appropriate fault condition and independent of any test facility incorporated in the device. Whilst the fault may be simulated by a simple test, reliable operation of the RCD is best ensured by using an RCD tester and applying the range of tests described below. Test results are recorded on the test result schedule.

The tests are made on the load side of the RCD, as near as practicable to its point of installation, and between the phase conductor of the protected circuit and the associated circuit protective conductor. The load supplied should be disconnected during the tests.

6.4.2 General purpose RCDs to BS 4293

(i) with a leakage current flowing equivalent to 50 % of the rated tripping current, the device should not open.

(ii) with a leakage current flowing equivalent to 100 % of the rated tripping current of the RCD, the device should open in less than 200 ms. Where the RCD incorporates an intentional time delay it should trip within a time range from '50 % of the rated time delay plus 200 ms' to '100 % of the rated time delay plus 200 ms'.

6.4.3 General purpose RCCBs to BS EN 61008 or RCBOs to BS EN 61009

(i) with a leakage current flowing equivalent to 50 % of the rated tripping current of the RCD the device should not open.

(ii) with a leakage current flowing equivalent to 100 % of the rated tripping current of the RCD, the device should open in less than 300 ms unless it is of 'Type S' (or selective) which incorporates an intentional time delay. In this case, it should trip within a time range from 130 ms to 500 ms.

6.4.4 RCD protected socket-outlets to BS 7288

(i) with a leakage current flowing equivalent to 50 % of the rated tripping current of the RCD the device should not open.

(ii) with a leakage current flowing equivalent to 100 % of the rated tripping current of the RCD, the device should open in less than 200 ms.

6.4.5 Additional requirement for supplementary protection

Where an RCD or RCBO with a rated residual operating current $I_{\Delta n}$ not exceeding 30 mA is used to provide supplementary protection against direct contact, with a test current of $5I_{\Delta n}$ the device should open in less than 40 ms. The maximum test time must not be longer than 40 ms, unless the protective conductor potential rises by less than 50 V. (The instrument supplier will advise on compliance.)

6.4.6 Integral test device

An integral test device is incorporated in each RCD. This device enables the electrical and mechanical parts of the RCD to be verified, by pressing the button marked 'T' or 'Test'. Operation of the integral test device does not provide a means of checking:

(a) the continuity of the earthing conductor or the associated circuit protective conductors, or

(b) any earth electrode or other means of earthing, or

(c) any other part of the associated installation earthing.

The test button will only operate the RCD if the RCD is energised.
Confirm that the notice to test RCDs quarterly (by pressing the test button) is fixed in a prominent position (see 3.4.8).

6.4.7 Test failure

If any test shows a failure to comply, the installation fault must be corrected. The test must then be repeated, as must any earlier test that could have been influenced by the failure.

Safe working 7

- **Safety and risk assessment**
- **Pre-work surveys**
- **Pre-work tests**
- **Isolation**
- **Defects in electrical installation**

7.1 Safety policy and risk assessment

The Electrotechnical Assessment Scheme for the technical competence of enterprises that undertake electrical installation work in dwellings requires that:

> The enterprise shall have a written health and safety policy statement and will carry out risk assessments as appropriate.

The Management of Health & Safety at Work Regulations require every employer to make a suitable and sufficient assessment of the risks the health and safety of his employees to which they are exposed while at work; and the risks to health and safety to persons not in his direct employment rising out of or in connection with the work being undertaken. The Health and Safety Executive has issued an approved Code of Practice – L21 to provide guidance on these risks. It is likely that all but the smallest of enterprises will need a copy of the approved code of practice and will need to prepare a written health and safety policy. Not only are industrial and commercial premises places of work, but dwellings are also places of work during construction, maintenance, repair and alteration and addition. The management of the electrical installation enterprise have responsibilities for their own staff and for others working on the site. It is important that all employees understand the commitment to safety of the enterprise and know the procedures they are expected to follow.

The following procedures for assessing the condition of the installation to be worked upon and the procedures to be followed for working are intended to help the managers of an enterprise in advising employees of the safety procedures to be followed. Typical safety procedures including non-electrical as well as electrical safety instructions and permit-to-work systems can be found in Appendix F.

7.2 Pre-work surveys

Part P in Section 2.1 requires that where an extension or a material alteration is made to an installation or there is a material change of use, the work must include for:

(i) Such works on the existing fixed electrical installation of the building as are necessary to enable the additions and alterations, the circuits which feed them, the protective measures and the relevant earthing and bonding systems to meet the requirements; and

(ii) Establishing that the mains supply equipment is suitable.

Section 2.2 of Part P says:

A way of complying would be to follow the guidance given in relation to design and installation to show that for the altered circumstances:

(a) The rating and the condition of the existing equipment belonging to both the consumer and the electricity distributor, can carry the additional loads being allowed for or are improved so that they can carry the additional loads being allowed for; and
(b) The correct protective measures are used; and
(c) The earthing and equipotential bonding arrangements are satisfactory.

7.3 Pre-work tests

Electricians should carry out the tests below before installation work is started. The tests should be carried out before any work is carried out including alterations and additions to existing installations, rewires and new installations (where applicable):

- Polarity
- Effectiveness of earthing
- Operation of earth leakage circuit-breakers (RCDs).

Deficiencies in the polarity and earthing arrangements must be rectified before work on the installation is commenced.

The procedures require all work other than certain specified tests to be carried out on dead electrical equipment. The Electricity at Work Regulations prohibit employees working on or near live equipment unless in all the circumstances it is unreasonable for it to be switched off. In a domestic premise there are most unlikely to be circumstances where it is unreasonable to make the equipment dead before working on it.

Before commencing work:

(1) Check that it is safe and acceptable to the persons in the premise to switch off the supply.

(2) Identify the electrical equipment to be worked on and the means of disconnection from all points of supply, e.g. by the opening of circuit-breakers, isolating switches, removal of fuses, links, or other suitable means. For a domestic installation, unless unreasonable in the circumstances, the main switch is opened and secured if necessary making the complete electrical installation dead.

(3) Isolate and prove. An approved test instrument, e.g. test lamp or voltage indicator, is used to verify that the installation or the part of the installation to be worked on is dead. The Electricity at Work Regulations do not allow live working (unless it is reasonable in the circumstances to work live). The procedure for isolating and proving is:

   (i) prove the operation of the test instrument by receiving positive indication the instrument works e.g. lamp glows with proving unit
   (ii) isolate the installation and secure the means of isolation
   (iii) test all the conductors of the isolated circuits for voltage to Earth with the test instrument. It should be confirmed that protective conductors are not live due, for example, to a wiring fault
   (iv) prove the operation of the test instrument again by receiving positive indication the tester works e.g. lamp glows with proving unit
   (v) if necessary for reasons of safety, earth the phase conductor with care, treating as live.

(4) Warning notices may need to be placed against interference.

(5) If there are persons in the property they must be advised that they must under no circumstances attempt to switch on the isolating device.

7.4 Isolation

Precautions need to be taken to prevent electrical equipment being made live inadvertently by others in the premises, particularly other electricians. This may be achieved by:

   (a) An approved lock
   (b) Removal of fuses or links
   (c) In the case of equipment, supplied from a plug and socket, removal of the plug from the socket-outlet. If the socket-outlet is not in view of the person carrying out the work, a suitable label warning against interference should be fixed or a lockable box employed.

As indicated above, the electrical equipment should be proved dead by the proper use of an approved voltage-testing device. Alternatively, clear evidence of isolation is needed, such as the physical tracing of the circuit and the physical identification of the means of isolation e.g. removal of the plug. On no account should reliance be placed on time switches, limit switches, lockout push buttons, etc.

7.5 Defects in electrical installations

Defects in an electrical installation identified before or during the work that affect the alterations or addition being carried out must be corrected before the work is completed, made live and certificates issued. Such work would include provision of adequate earthing arrangements, and the installation of suitable residual current devices.

Defects identified in an installation that do not affect the alteration, addition or extension being carried out are required to be notified in writing to the householder. The notification should be confirmed on the completion certificate.

Maintenance 8

- **The need for maintenance**
- **Domestic installations**
- **Purpose of periodic inspection**
- **Periodic Inspection Reports**

8.1 The need for maintenance

Regulation 4(2) of the Electricity at Work Regulations 1989 requires that:

As may be necessary to prevent danger, all systems shall be maintained so as to prevent, so far as is reasonably practicable, such danger.

Regulation 4(2) of the Electricity at Work Regulations makes reference to all systems being maintained so as to prevent, so far as is reasonably practicable, such danger. Systems are defined as follows:

"System" means an electrical system in which all the electrical equipment is, or may be electrically connected to a common source of electrical energy and includes such source and such equipment (Regulation 2(1)).

"Electrical equipment" includes anything used, intended to be used or installed for use, to generate, provide, transmit, transform, rectify, convert, conduct, distribute, control, store, measure or use electrical energy. (Regulation 2(1)).

It is clear that as a consequence of these definitions, "system" includes all electrical equipment including the generating equipment, the fixed wiring of a building, and all the equipment in the building including fixed, portable and hand-held appliances. Electrical equipment includes anything powered by whatever source of electrical energy including battery-powered.

8.2 Domestic installations

Domestic installations are within the compass of the Electricity at Work Act when persons are at work, that is employed to work in the premises, otherwise they are not. However, the same basic principles apply as are appropriate to places of work, in that maintenance of domestic installation would comprise:

(a) Routine checks
(b) Periodic inspection and, as necessary, testing.

In a user manual a householder must be advised that as well as a professional periodic inspection and test at least every ten years, all defects must be repaired as they arise. If there are signs of wear, overheating, looseness, or difficulty in operating equipment then an electrician should be instructed to inspect the installation and maintain as necessary.

8.3 Purpose of periodic inspection

The purpose of periodic inspection and testing of an electrical installation is to determine, so far as is reasonably practicable, whether the installation is in a satisfactory condition for continued use. This does not necessarily mean compliance with all the latest requirements of BS 7671.

BS 7671 requires an inspection comprising a careful scrutiny of the installation to be carried out without dismantling or with partial dismantling as required, together with appropriate tests.

The purpose of the inspection and testing as stated in BS 7671 is to provide so far as reasonably practicable for:

(1) The safety of persons and livestock against the effects of electric shock and burns, and
(2) Protection against damage to property by fire and heat arising from installation defects,
(3) Confirmation that the installation is not damaged or deteriorated so as to impair safety, and
(4) The identification of installation defects and non-compliance with the Wiring Regulations (BS 7671) which may give rise to danger.

It is to be noted that the essence of periodic inspection is to identify those defects that may give rise to danger.

8.4 Periodic Inspection Reports

Appendix 6 of BS 7671 includes a Periodic Inspection Report complete with notes for the inspector and for the recipient of the report. The following forms are as in BS 7671 except they have been completed for a "typical" periodic inspection and test.

Periodic Inspection report forms complete with inspection and test schedules may be downloaded from the IEE **website: www.iee.org.uk**

8.4.1 Typical periodic inspection report

Form F 6 Form No 126 /6

PERIODIC INSPECTION REPORT FOR AN ELECTRICAL INSTALLATION (note 1)

(REQUIREMENTS FOR ELECTRICAL INSTALLATIONS - BS 7671 [IEE WIRING REGULATIONS])

DETAILS OF THE CLIENT

Client: Mr A Brown

Address: 111, Any Street, Town, County NT7 8BS

Purpose for which this Report is required: Mortgage (note 3)

DETAILS OF THE INSTALLATION Tick boxes as appropriate

Occupier: As above

Installation: As above

Address: As above

Description of Premises: Domestic ☑ Commercial ☐ Industrial ☐ Other ☐

House with garage

Estimated age of the Electrical Installation: 15 years

Evidence of Alterations or Additions: Yes ☑ No ☐ Not apparent ☐

If "Yes", estimate age: 5 years

Date of last inspection: — Records available Yes ☐ No ☑

EXTENT AND LIMITATIONS OF THE INSPECTION (note 5)

Extent of electrical installation covered by this report: installation to house, garage and garden shed

Limitations: ~~No dismantling or lifting of floorboards~~

This inspection has been carried out in accordance with BS 7671: 2001 (IEE Wiring Regulations), amended to 2004. Cables concealed within trunking and conduits, or cables and conduits concealed under floors, in roof spaces and generally within the fabric of the building or underground have not been inspected.

NEXT INSPECTION (note 8)

I/We recommend that this installation is further inspected and tested after an interval of not more than 10 ~~months~~/years, provided that any observations 'requiring urgent attention' are attended to without delay.

DECLARATION

INSPECTED AND TESTED BY

Name: W White Signature: W White

For and on behalf of: County Electrics Position: Electrician

Address: 187 Industrial Lane
Town
County MP3 8BQ

Date: 18/4/2005

Page 1 of 4

▲ Page 1 of a periodic inspection report

SUPPLY CHARACTERISTICS AND EARTHING ARRANGEMENTS Tick boxes and enter details, as appropriate

Earthing arrangements	Number and Type of Live Conductors	Nature of Supply Parameters	Supply Protective Device Characteristics
TN-C ☐ TN-S ☐ TN-C-S ☑ TT ☐ IT ☐ Alternative source ☐ of supply (to be detailed on attached schedules)	a.c. ☑ d.c. ☐ 1-phase, 2-wire ☑ 2-pole ☐ 1-phase, 3 wire ☐ 3-pole ☐ 2-phase, 3-wire ☐ other ☐ 3-phase, 3-wire ☐ 3-phase, 4-wire ☐	Nominal voltage, U/U_o (1) ....230..... V Nominal frequency, f (1) ....50..... Hz Prospective fault current, I_{pf} (2) ....1.0... kA (note 4) External loop impedance, Z_e (2) ...0.24 Ω *(Note: (1) by enquiry, (2) by enquiry or by measurement)*	Type: BS 1361 fuse Nominal current rating ....100.....A

PARTICULARS OF INSTALLATION REFERRED TO IN THE REPORT Tick boxes and enter details, as appropriate

Means of Earthing
Distributor's facility ☑
Installation earth electrode ☐

Details of Installation Earth Electrode (*where applicable)*

Type (e.g. rod(s), tape etc)	Location	Electrode resistance to earth
—	—	— Ω

Main Protective Conductors

Earthing conductor: material ....Copper..... csa ......10..mm² connection verified ☑
Main equipotential bonding conductors material ....Copper..... csa ......6..mm² connection verified ☑

To incoming water service ☑ To incoming gas service ☑ To incoming oil service ☐ To structural steel ☐
To lightning protection ☐ To other incoming service(s) ☐ (state details...)

Main Switch or Circuit-breaker

BS, Type...5486.......................... No. of poles ...2...... Current rating ..80.....A Voltage rating ......240..V
Location....Meter cupboard.................................. Fuse rating or setting .—.....A
Rated residual operating current $I_{\Delta n}$ = ...—... mA, and operating time of ...—.. ms (at $I_{\Delta n}$) (applicable only where an RCD is suitable and is used as a main circuit-breaker)

OBSERVATIONS AND RECOMMENDATIONS Tick boxes as appropriate (note 9)

Referring to the attached Schedule(s) of Inspection and Test Results, and subject to the limitations specified at the Extent and Limitations of the Inspection section

☐ No remedial work is required ☑ The following observations are made:

Observation	Recommendations as detailed below note 6
Main bonding conductors sized per 15th edition	4
No 30 mA RCD to socket in garage	1
No 30 mA RCD to socket in shed	1
Light pendants and lampholders worn/faulty	1
No supplementary bonding in bathroom	2
Broken socket in lounge	1

One of the following numbers, as appropriate, is to be allocated to each of the observations made above to indicate to the person(s) responsible for the installation the action recommended.

1 requires urgent attention 2 requires improvement 3 requires further investigation

4 does not comply with BS 7671: 2001 amended to 2004 This does not imply that the electrical installation inspected is unsafe.

SUMMARY OF THE INSPECTION (note 7)

Date(s) of the inspection: ......28/6/2005..........
General condition of the installation: ....Urgent repairs and improvements required........

Overall assessment: ~~Satisfactory~~/Unsatisfactory (note 8)

SCHEDULE(S)

The attached Schedules are part of this document and this Report is only valid when they are attached to it.

......1.... Schedule(s) of Inspections and .....1..... Schedule(s) of Test Results are attached.
(Enter quantities of schedules attached).

Page 2 of 4

▲ Page 2 of a periodic inspection report

NOTES ON THE PERIODIC INSPECTION REPORT

1. This Periodic Inspection Report form shall only be used for the reporting on the condition of an existing installation.

2. The Report, normally comprising at least four pages, shall include schedules of both the inspection and the test results. Additional sheets of test results may be necessary for other than a simple installation. The page numbers of each sheet shall be indicated, together with the total number of sheets involved. The Report is only valid if a Schedule of Inspections and a Schedule of Test Results are appended.

3. The intended purpose of the Periodic Inspection Report shall be identified, together with the recipient's details in the appropriate boxes.

4. The maximum prospective fault current recorded should be the greater of either the short-circuit current or the earth fault current.

5. The 'Extent and Limitations' box shall fully identify the elements of the installation that are covered by the report and those that are not; this aspect having been agreed with the client and other interested parties before the inspection and testing is carried out.

6. The recommendation(s), if any, shall be categorised using the numbered coding 1 – 4 as appropriate.

7. The 'Summary of the Inspection' box shall clearly identify the condition of the installation in terms of safety.

8. Where the periodic inspection and testing has resulted in a satisfactory overall assessment, the time interval for the next periodic inspection and testing shall be given. The IEE Guidance Note 3 provides guidance on the maximum interval between inspections for various types of buildings. If the inspection and testing reveal that parts of the installation require urgent attention, it would be appropriate to state an earlier re-inspection date having due regard to the degree of urgency and extent of the necessary remedial work.

9. If the space available on the periodic inspection form for information on recommendations is insufficient, additional pages shall be provided as necessary.

PERIODIC INSPECTION REPORT
GUIDANCE FOR RECIPIENTS (to be appended to the Report)

This Periodic Inspection Report form is intended for reporting on the condition of an existing electrical installation.

You should have received an original Report and the contractor should have retained a duplicate. If you were the person ordering this Report, but not the owner of the installation, you should pass this Report, or a copy of it, immediately to the owner.

The original Report is to be retained in a safe place and should be shown to any person inspecting or undertaking work on the electrical installation in the future. If you later vacate the property, this Report will provide the new owner with details of the condition of the electrical installation at the time the Report was issued.

The 'Extent and Limitations' box should fully identify the extent of the installation covered by this Report and any limitations on the inspection and tests. The contractor should have agreed these aspects with you and with any other interested parties (Licensing Authority, Insurance Company, Building Society etc) before the inspection was carried out.

The Report will usually contain a list of recommended actions necessary to bring the installation up to the current standard. For items classified as 'requires urgent attention', the safety of those using the installation may be at risk, and it is recommended that a competent person undertakes the necessary remedial work without delay.

For safety reasons, the electrical installation will need to be re-inspected at appropriate intervals by a competent person. The maximum time interval recommended before the next inspection is stated in the Report under 'Next Inspection.'

The Report is only valid if a Schedule of Inspections and a Schedule of Test Results is appended.

Form F3 Form No 126/3

SCHEDULE OF INSPECTIONS

Methods of protection against electric shock

(a) Protection against both direct and indirect contact:

- N/A (i) SELV (note 1)
- N/A (ii) Limitation of discharge of energy (note 2)

(b) Protection against direct contact: (note 3)

- ✓ (i) Insulation of live parts
- X (ii) Barriers or enclosures
- N/A (iii) Obstacles (note 4)
- N/A (iv) Placing out of reach (note 5)
- N/A (v) PELV (note 6)
- X (vi) Presence of RCD for supplementary protection

(c) Protection against indirect contact:

(i) EEBAD (note 7) including:

- ✓ Presence of earthing conductor
- ✓ Presence of circuit protective conductors
- ✓ Presence of main equipotential bonding conductors
- X Presence of supplementary equipotential bonding conductors
- N/A Presence of earthing arrangements for combined protective and functional purposes (note 8)
- N/A Presence of adequate arrangements for alternative source(s), where applicable
- N/A Presence of residual current device(s)
- N/A (ii) Use of Class II equipment or equivalent insulation (note 9)
- N/A (iii) Non-conducting location: (note 10) Absence of protective conductors
- N/A (iv) Earth-free equipotential bonding: (note 11) Presence of earth-free equipotential bonding conductors
- N/A (v) Electrical separation (note 12)

Prevention of mutual detrimental influence

- ✓ (a) Proximity of non-electrical services and other influences
- ✓ (b) Segregation of band I and band II circuits or band II insulation used
- ✓ (c) Segregation of safety circuits

Identification

- ✓ (a) Presence of diagrams, instructions, circuit charts and similar information
- ✓ (b) Presence of danger notices and other warning notices
- ✓ (c) Labelling of protective devices, switches and terminals
- ✓ (d) Identification of conductors

Cables and conductors

- ✓ (a) Routing of cables in prescribed zones or within mechanical protection
- ✓ (b) Connection of conductors
- ✓ (c) Erection methods
- ✓ (d) Selection of conductors for current-carrying capacity and voltage drop
- ✓ (e) Presence of fire barriers, suitable seals and protection against thermal effects

General

- ✓ (a) Presence and correct location of appropriate devices for isolation and switching
- ✓ (b) Adequacy of access to switchgear and other equipment
- X (c) Particular protective measures for special installations and locations
- ✓ (d) Connection of single-pole devices for protection or switching in phase conductors only
- ✓ (e) Correct connection of accessories and equipment
- N/A (f) Presence of undervoltage protective devices
- ✓ (g) Choice and setting of protective and monitoring devices for protection against indirect contact and/or overcurrent
- X (h) Selection of equipment and protective measures appropriate to external influences
- ✓ (i) Selection of appropriate functional switching devices

Inspected by W White Date 18/4/2005

Notes:

✓ to indicate an inspection has been carried out and the result is satisfactory

X to indicate an inspection has been carried out and the result was unsatisfactory

N/A to indicate the inspection is not applicable

LIM to indicate that, exceptionally, a limitation agreed with the person ordering the work prevented the inspection or test being carried out.

1. SELV An extra-low voltage system which is electrically separate from earth and from other systems. The particular requirements of the Regulations must be checked (see Regulations 411-02 and 471-02)
2. Limitation of discharge of energy - not adopted for domestic installations, used on appliances and equipment.
3. Method of protection against direct contact - will include measurement of distances where appropriate.
4. Obstacles - not suitable for domestic installations, only adopted in special circumstances (see Regulations 412-04 and 471-06)
5. Placing out of reach - not suitable for domestic installations, only adopted in special circumstances (see Regulations 412-05 and 471-07)
6. PELV An extra-low voltage system which is electrically separate from other systems but not earth. The particular requirements of the Regulations must be checked (see Regulations 411-02 and 471-14)
7. EEBAD Earthed equipotential bonding and automatic disconnection of supply, the common form of indirect shock protection
8. Combined protective and functional earthing - it is normal to combine protective and functional earthing. In non-domestic systems functional earthing of IT systems may be separated, (clean earth).
9. Use of Class II equipment - not suitable for domestic installations, infrequently adopted and only when the installation is to be supervised (see Regulations 413-03 and 471-09)
10. Non-conducting locations - not suitable for domestic installations and requiring special precautions (see Regulations 413-04 and 471-10)
11. Earth-free local equipotential bonding - not suitable for domestic installations, only used in special circumstances (see Regulations 413-05 and 471-14)
12. Electrical separation - not adopted in domestic installations (see Regulations 413-06 and 471-12)

Page 3 of 4

▲ Page 3, schedule of inspections, F3 of the periodic inspection report

Form 4

Form No 126/4

SCHEDULE OF TEST RESULTS

Contractor: County Electrics
Test Date: 18/4/2005
Signature: W White
Method of protection against indirect contact:
Equipment vulnerable to testing:

Address/Location of distribution board:
111 Any Street

* Type of Supply: ~~TN-S~~/TN-C-S/~~TT~~
* Ze at origin: 0.24 ohms
* PFC: 1.0 kA

Instruments
loop impedance: LM
continuity: LM 11
insulation: LM 14
RCD tester: LM 16

Description of Work: House, Garage and Shed

Circuit Description	Overcurrent Device * Short-circuit capacity: 6 kA		Wiring Conductors		Test Results										
					Continuity			Insulation Resistance		Polarity	Earth Loop Impedance Z_s	Functional Testing		Remarks
	type	Rating I_n A	live mm²	cpc mm²	$R_1 + R_2$ Ω	R_2 Ω	Ring	Live/Live MΩ	Live/Earth MΩ		Ω	RCD time ms	Other	
1	2	3	4	5	*6	*7	*8	*9	*10	*11	*12	*13	*14	15
1 Lights up	fuse	5	1.5	1.0	✓			10	8	✓	1.3	—	✓	faulty pendants
2 Lights down	"	5	1.5	1.0	✓	—	—	—	7	✓	1.2	—	✓	faulty pendants
3 Ring up	"	30	2.5	1.5	✓	—	✓	15	15	✓	0.7	—	✓	
4 Ring down	"	30	2.5	1.5	✓	—	✓	12	12	✓	0.8	—	✓	no RCD
5 Cooker	"	30	6.0	2.5	✓	—	—	20	15	✓	0.4	—	✓	
6 Immersion heater	"	15	2.5	1.5	✓	—	—	20	15	✓	0.4	—	✓	
7 Shower	"	30	6.0	2.5	✓	—	—	20	15	✓	0.3	—	✓	

Deviations from Wiring Regulations and special notes: Main bonding cables too small,
no supplementary bonding to bathroom,
no RCD to ground floor sockets
lighting pendants need replacing.

* See notes on schedule of test results

Page 4 of 4

▲ Page 4, schedule of test results, F4 of the periodic inspection report

NOTES ON THE SCHEDULE OF TEST RESULTS

***Type of supply** is ascertained from the distributor or by inspection.

***Ze at origin.** Preferably the maximum value declared by the distributor is inserted. For PME (TN-C-S) domestic single phase supplies the value will not exceed 0.35 Ω. The effectiveness of the earth must be confirmed by a test. If measured, the main bonding will need to be disconnected for the duration of the test.

***Short-circuit capacity** of the protective device is noted.
Consumer units including protective devices complying as a whole assembly with BS EN 60439-3 (Including Annex ZA) or BS 5486-13 are suitable for locations with fault currents up to 16 kA when supplied through a type II fuse to BS 1361 : 1971 (1992) rated at no more than 100 A. Otherwise see Table 7.2A of the On-Site Guide or 2.7.15 of GN3.

***Prospective fault current (pfc).** The value recorded is the greater of either the short-circuit current or the earth fault current. Preferably determined by enquiry from the distributor. For domestic supplies, except for London and some other major city centres, the maximum fault current for 230 V single-phase supplies up to 100 A will not exceed 16 kA.

The following tests, where relevant, must be carried out in the following sequence:

Continuity of protective conductors, including main and supplementary bonding.

Every protective conductor, including main and supplementary bonding conductors, should be tested to verify that they are continuous and correctly connected.

Column 6 Continuity
Where Test Method 1 is used, enter the measured resistance of the phase conductor plus the circuit protective conductor ($R_1 + R_2$). See 6.3.4 or 10.3.1 of the On-Site Guide or 2.7.5 of GN3.

During the continuity testing (Test Method 1) the following polarity checks are to be carried out:

(a) Every fuse and single-pole control and protective device is connected in the phase conductor only
(b) Centre-contact bayonet and Edison screw lampholders have the outer contact connected to the neutral conductor
(c) Wiring is correctly connected to socket-outlets and similar accessories.

Compliance is to be indicated by a tick in polarity column 11.
($R_1 + R_2$) need not be recorded if R_2 is recorded in column 7.

Column 7 Where Test Method 2 is used, the maximum value of R_2 is recorded in column 7.
Where the alternative method of Regulation 413-02-12 is used for shock protection, the resistance of the circuit protective conductor R_2 is measured and recorded in column 7.
See 6.3.4 or 10.3.1 of the On-Site Guide or 2.7.5 of GN3.

Column 8 Continuity of ring final conductors
A test shall be made to verify the continuity of each conductor including the protective conductor of every ring final circuit.

See 6.3.5 or 10.3.2 of the On-Site Guide or 2.7.6 of GN3.

Columns 9 and 10 Insulation Resistance
All voltage sensitive devices to be disconnected or test between live conductors (phase and neutral) connected together and earth.

The insulation resistance between live conductors is to be inserted in column 9.

The minimum insulation resistance values are given in Table 10.1 of the On-Site Guide or Table 2.2 of GN3.

See 6.3.6 or 10.3.3(iv) of the On-Site Guide or 2.7.7 of GN3.

All the preceding tests should be carried out before the installation is energised.

Column 11 Polarity
A satisfactory polarity test should be indicated by a tick in column 11.

Only in a Schedule of Test Results associated with a Periodic Inspection Report is it acceptable to record incorrect polarity.

Column 12 Earth fault loop impedance Zs
This may be determined either by direct measurement at the furthest point of a live circuit or by adding (R_1 + R_2) of column 6 to Ze. Ze is determined by measurement at the origin of the installation or preferably the value declared by the distributor used. $Z_s = Z_e + (R_1 + R_2)$. Zs should be less than the values given in the circuit tables in Chapter 4 or Appendix 2 of the On-Site Guide or Appendix 2 of GN3.

Column 13 Functional testing
The operation of RCDs (including RCBOs) shall be tested by simulating a fault condition, independent of any test facility in the device.

Record operating time in column 13. Effectiveness of the test button must be confirmed. See 6.4 or Section 11 of the On-Site Guide or 2.7.16 of GN3.

Column 14 All switchgear and controlgear assemblies, drives, control and interlocks, etc must be operated to ensure that they are properly mounted, adjusted, and installed.

Satisfactory operation is indicated by a tick in column 14.

Earth electrode resistance
The earth electrode resistance of TT installations must be measured, and normally an RCD is required.

For reliability in service the resistance of any earth electrode should be below 200 Ω. Record the value on Forms 1, 2 or 6 as appropriate. See 6.3.8 or 10.3.5 of the On-Site Guide or 2.7.13 of GN3.

8.4.2 Observations and recommendations

The periodic inspection form in BS 7671 includes notes for guidance. Within the observation and recommendations section each observation is required to be allocated a number as follows:

(1) Requires urgent attention

(2) Requires improvement

(3) Requires further investigation

(4) Does not comply with BS 7671, 2001 amended to (date). This does not imply the electrical installation is unsafe.

The electrician carrying out the inspection and test is required to provide an overall assessment as to whether the installation is satisfactory or unsatisfactory. It is entirely a matter for the competent person conducting the inspection to decide on the recommendation code to be given to a given observation. The person's own judgement as a competent person should not be unduly influenced by the client. Remember that the person signing the report is responsible for its content. He is required to give advice to the householder as to any repairs necessary to make the installation satisfactory, that is safe. Installations with no category 1, 2 or 3 observations can be considered satisfactory.

1 Requires urgent attention:

Broken equipment where live parts are exposed
No earth connection at origin
Use of water or gas pipe as a means of earthing
Double-pole fusing
RCD that does not operate when test button is pressed
No circuit protective conductor in one or more lighting circuits with Class I light fittings. (Class I light fittings must be earthed)
Incorrect polarity

2 Requires improvement:

No RCD protection for socket-outlets likely to supply portable equipment outdoors
No main equipotential bonding
No supplementary bonding in bathroom
No circuit protective conductor in one or more lighting circuits with Class II light fittings. (Class II light fittings do not require to be earthed)

3 Requires further investigation:

Not normally applicable to domestic installations where necessary information on the installation and equipment is normally readily available

4 Does not comply with BS 7671, 2001 amended to (date). This does not imply the electrical installation and inspection is unsafe:

Main bonding conductor size 6 mm^2 in a TN-C-S installation
Bathroom supplementary bonding does not include lighting circuits with Class II fittings
Voltage operated earth leakage trip installed

Three-phase supplies 9

- Electricity distribution
- Dwellings
- Characteristics of three-phase supplies
- Fault levels
- Design

This Chapter gives a brief introduction to three-phase electricity supplies.

9.1 Electricity distribution

With particular exceptions in rural areas, electricity is distributed at low voltage by a three-phase distribution system with 230 V a.c. nominal voltage to earth and 400 V a.c. nominal voltage between phases at a frequency of 50 cycles. Depending on the load of the building either a single-phase or a three-phase supply will be provided by the electricity distributor.

9.2 Dwellings

Individual dwellings will be supplied at single-phase unless the demand of the premises is high (say an after diversity demand over 15 kW), or due to network conditions. Whilst individual flats in a development will almost certainly be supplied at single-phase, the supply brought into the building is likely to be three-phase. A typical PME installation in a block of flats is shown in Figure 9.2.

9.3 Characteristics of three-phase supplies

The physical construction of three-phase generators results in the peak voltage of each of the three phases of a three-phase supply being displaced in time by 120 degrees, as shown in Figure 9.3. The result is that the voltage between phases is not 2 x 230 volts as any two phases are never at their peak at the same time, but $\sqrt{3}$ x 230 i.e. 400 volts.

▼ **Figure 9.2** Three-phase PME supply to flats

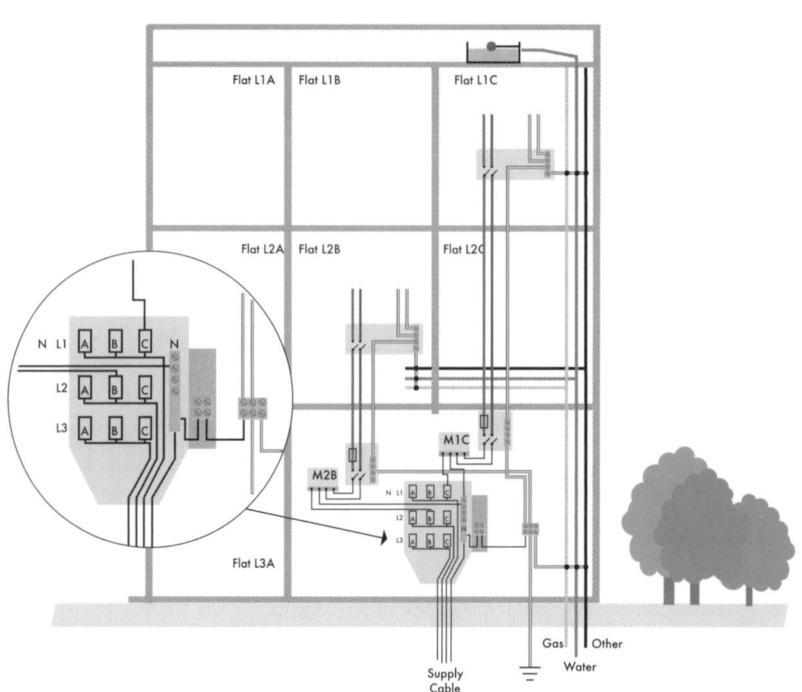

The currents in each phase of a three-phase supply (for a symmetrical load) are similarly 120 degrees out of phase. The neutral currents of each phase of a three-phase supply return in a common neutral. If the loads are symmetrical and balanced the total neutral current will be zero. This clearly has particular benefits for electricity distribution in that it significantly reduces voltage drop and energy losses.

> **Note:** For loads generating triple harmonics as may be found in computer power supplies and electronic controls to lighting, the neutral currents may not sum to zero but add. These discussions are outside the scope of this Guide; for further information refer to the IEE publication – The Commentary on the IEE Wiring Regulations.

9.4 Fault levels

In the event of a fault, particularly a three-phase fault to earth, the fault current flowing for a three-phase supply will

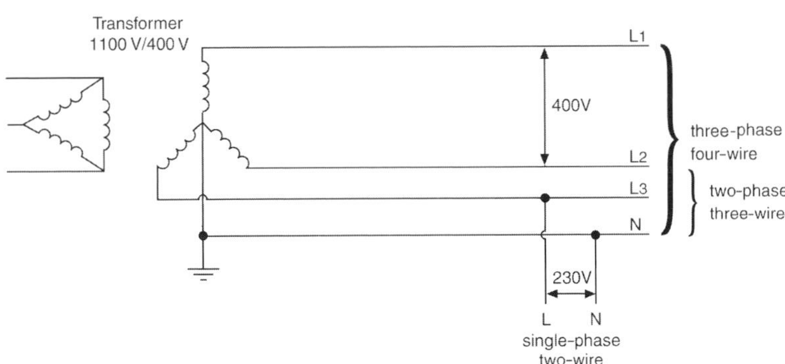

▲ **Figure 9.3.1** Three-phase supply voltages

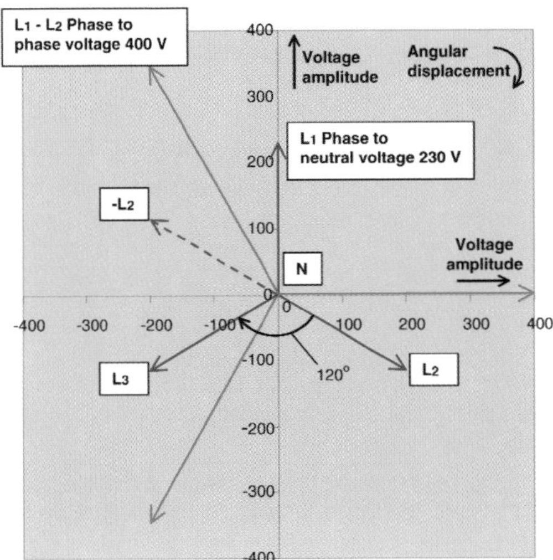

◀ **Figure 9.3.2** Three-phase voltages, with angular displacement

be considerably in excess of that for a single-phase installation. Three-phase equipment will generally require a higher fault rating than single-phase. Fault levels may be 18 kA (0.5pf) at the connection of the service line to the LV distribution main and 25 kA (0.23p.f.) at the point of connection to the busbars in the distribution substation.

Single-phase earth fault loop impedance testers are unlikely to give an accurate indication of fault levels, particularly close up to the origin of a three-phase supply. However, for general guidance fault levels should be estimated as being twice that indicated by a single-phase to earth fault loop impedance tester (a brief explanation would be that the loop

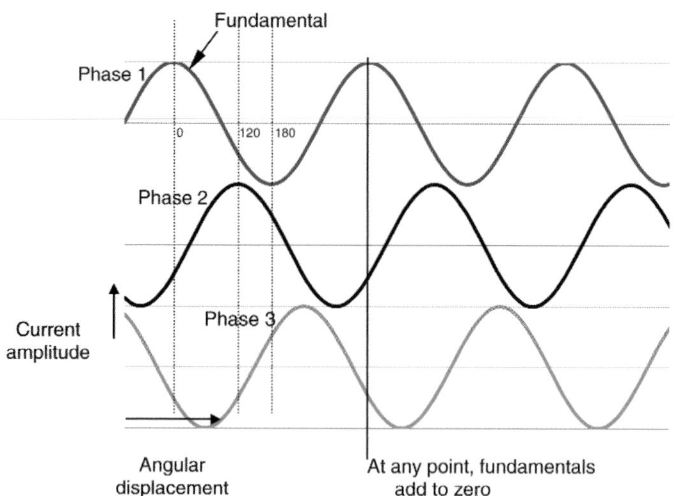

▲ **Figure 9.3.3** Current waveform

impedance tester makes a measurement using single-phase test currents; a three-phase short circuit fault is likely to result in currents of at least double these as the balanced nature of the fault may result in there being in effect no neutral impedance).

9.5 Design

In the design of a three-phase installation it is particularly important that there be a clear plan and logic to the electrical installation to facilitate safe working during maintenance. Identifiable locations should be supplied from the same fuse board and particular care taken in labelling. Where equipment in a particular location is supplied from more than one fuse board and more than one phase, then there needs to be careful labelling to make clear to electricians carrying out subsequent maintenance that it may be necessary to isolate more than one fuse board or more than one phase of the supply.

Note: With a three-phase supply, whilst the voltage between phases is 400 volts the voltage to earth remains at 230 volts.

There are particular hazards associated with short-circuits in three-phase supplies; for example arcs can cause melting and ionising. Care has to be taken when using multi-range instruments on three-phase supplies, particularly if the instruments do not have fused leads or are not similarly protected.

Other Building Regulations 10

- **Structure** (Approved document A)
- **Fire safety** (Approved document B)
- **Site preparation** (Approved document C)
- **Resistance to the passage of sound** (Approved document E)
- **Ventilation** (Approved document F)
- **Conservation of fuel and power** (Approved document L1)
- **Access and facilities for the disabled** (Approved document M)

Apart from Part P which is concerned specifically with the safety of fixed electrical installations, there are other requirements in the Building Regulations that affect the electrical installation. Included are:

Approved document A – Structure (depth of chases in walls, and size of holes and notches in floor and roof joists)

Approved document B – Fire safety (fire safety of certain electrical installations; provision of fire alarm and fire detection systems; fire resistance of penetrations through floors and walls)

Approved document C – Site preparation and resistance to contaminants and moisture (moisture resistance of cable penetrations through external walls)

Approved document E – Resistance to the passage of sound (penetrations through floors and walls)

Approved document F – Ventilation (ventilation rates for dwellings)

Approved document L1 – Conservation of fuel and power (energy efficient lighting)

Approved document M – Access and facilities for disabled people (heights of switches and socket-outlets)

10.1 Structure (Approved document A)

The requirement of Part A is shown below

Requirement	*Limits on application*
Loading **A1.** – (1) The building shall be constructed so that the combined dead, imposed and wind loads are sustained and transmitted by it to the ground – (a) safely; and (b) without causing such deflection or deformation of any part of the building, or such movement of the ground, as will impair the stability of any part of another building. (2) In assessing whether a building complies with sub paragraph(1) regard shall be had to the imposed and wind loads to which it is likely to be subjected in the ordinary course of its use for the purpose for which it is intended.	
Ground Movement **A2.** The building shall be constructed so that ground movement caused by:- (a) swelling, shrinkage or freezing of the subsoil; or (b) land-slip or subsidence (other than subsidence arising from shrinkage), in so far as the risk can be reasonably foreseen, will not impair the stability of any part of the building.	

The basic requirement for those installing electrical installations in a building is not to cut, drill, chase, penetrate or in any way interfere with the structure so as to cause significant reduction in its load bearing capability.

Approved document A provides practical guidance as below.

10.1.1 Notches and holes in simply supported floor and roof joists

(A section 1B6)

Notches should be no deeper than 0.125 times the depth of a joist and should not be cut closer to the support than 0.07 of the span and not further away from the support than 0.25 times the span.

Holes should be:

- no greater diameter than 0.25 times the depth of the joist
- drilled at the neutral axis
- not less than 3 diameters (centre to centre) apart and
- located between 0.25 and 0.4 times the span from the support.

Table 10.1.1 Joist and stud notch and drill limits

Item	Location	Maximum size
Notching joists	top edge, 0.07 to 0.25 of span	0.125 x depth of joist
Drilling joists	centre line, 0.25 to 0.4 of span	0.25 x depth of joist

No notches or holes should be cut into the roof rafters, other than at supports where the rafter may be birdsmouthed to a depth not exceeding 0.33 times the rafter depth.

► **Figure 10.1.1** Notches and holes in wooden joists

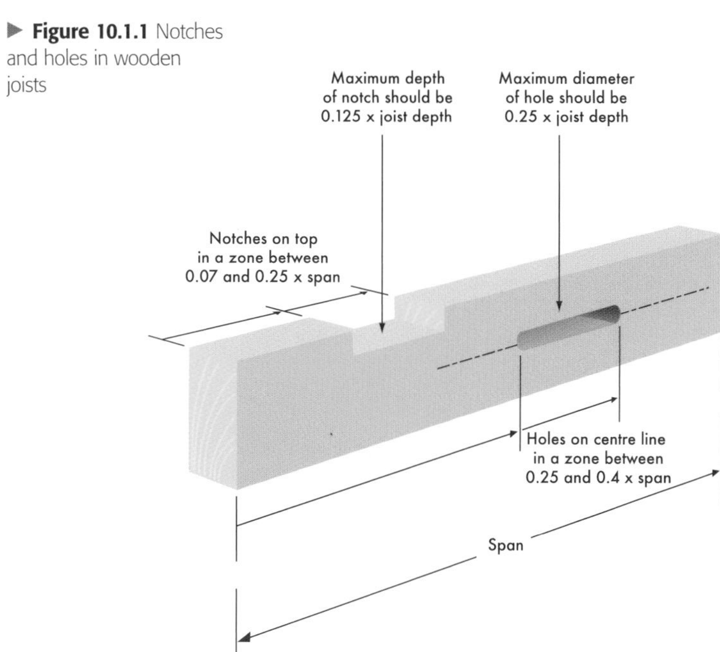

Notes:
1. Maximum diameter of hole should be 0.25 x joist depth.
2. Holes on centre line in a zone between 0.25 and 0.4 x span.
3. Maximum depth of notch should be 0.125 x joist depth.
4. Notches on top in a zone between 0.07 and 0.25 x span.
5. Holes in the same joist should be at least 3 diameters apart.

▶ **Figure 10.1.2** Chases in walls

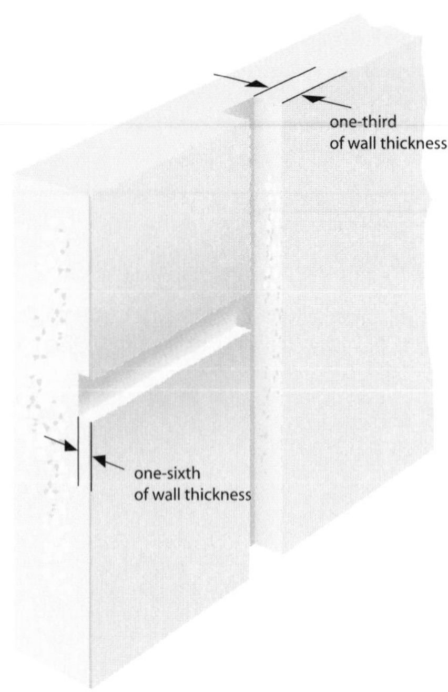

10.1.2 Chases

(Part A section 1C 31).

Vertical chases should not be deeper than one-third of the wall thickness or in cavity walls one-third of the thickness of the leaf.

Horizontal chases should not be deeper than one-sixth of the thickness of the leaf or wall.

Chases should not be so positioned as to impair the stability of the wall particularly where hollow blocks are used.

10.2 Fire Safety (Approved document B)

The requirement of Part B is shown below

Requirement	*Limits on application*
Means of warning and escape **B1.** The building shall be designed and constructed so that there are appropriate provisions for the early warning of fire, and appropriate means of escape in case of fire from the building to a place of safety outside the building capable of being safely and effectively used at all material times	Requirement B1 does not apply to any prison provided under section 33 of the Prisons Act 1952 (power to provide prisons etc.)

Approved document B states "In the Secretary of State's view the requirement of B1 will be met if:

(a) there are routes of sufficient number and capacity, which are suitably located to enable persons to escape to a place of safety in the event of fire;

(b) the routes are sufficiently protected from the effects of fire by enclosure where necessary;

(c) the routes are adequately lit;

(d) the exits are suitably signed; and if

(e) there are appropriate facilities to either limit the ingress of smoke to the escape route(s) or to restrict the fire and remove smoke;

all to an extent necessary that is dependent on the use of the building, its size and height; and

(f) there is sufficient means for giving early warning of fire for persons in the building."

Advice on meeting these requirements is outside the scope of this Guide other than guidance on single dwelling units.

10.2.1 Automatic fire detection and alarm systems in single dwellings

If dwellings are not protected by automatic fire detection and alarm systems in accordance with BS 5839 Part 1 or BS 5839 Part 6, they are required to be provided with a suitable number of smoke alarms.

(a) Smoke alarms in single dwellings

The Building Regulations 1991 and the Building Standards (Scotland) Regulations 1990 require all new and refurbished dwellings to be fitted with mains operated smoke alarms. The requirements for single family dwellings of not more than two storeys are that self-contained smoke alarms should be installed as follows:

(1) at least one on each floor

(2) within 7 m of kitchens and living rooms or other areas where fires may start e.g. integral garages

(3) within 3 m of all bedroom doors.

The smoke alarm must be installed in accordance with the manufacturer's instructions, generally on ceilings and at least 300 mm from any wall or ceiling luminaire.

The alarms are required to:

- be interconnected so that detection of smoke by one unit operates the alarm in all units
- be permanently wired to a separate way in the distribution board (consumer unit), or supplied from a local, regularly-used lighting circuit
- have battery backup.

The smoke alarm circuit should preferably not be protected by any residual current device (RCD). However, if electrical safety requires the use of RCD, either:

- the smoke alarm circuit should be protected by a single RCD which serves no other circuit; or
- the RCD protection of a smoke alarm circuit should operate independently of any RCD protection for circuits supplying socket-outlets or portable equipment.

See Figure 3 in Chapter 3.

The cable for the power supply to each self-contained unit and the inter-connecting cable need have no fire retardant properties, and need no special segregation. Otherwise, fire alarm system cables generally are required to be segregated as per BS 5839-1 and BS 5839-6. See Table 10.2.

(b) Larger houses, loft conversions, flats and maisonettes

Persons carrying out designs of larger houses, loft conversions, flats and maisonettes will need to make reference to B1, Section 1, of Approved document B which is reproduced in Appendix C of this Guide.

10.2.2 Spread of fire

Part B requires precautions to be taken to inhibit the spread of fire within a building and has requirements for the internal linings that they should adequately resist the spread of flame over their surfaces and have, if ignited, a rate of heat release which is reasonable in the circumstances. This sets classifications for lining of walls and ceilings and roof lights, which must be adopted by installers. It is also particularly applicable to thermo-plastic materials, which include lighting diffusers forming part of the ceiling. See Appendix C.

When carrying out electrical installations in a building the installer must not degrade the precautions taken or building design features intended to limit the spread of fire or limit the propagation of smoke and fumes.

Cable trunking and ducting may require sealing and luminaires penetrating ceilings may require fitting with fire resistant hoods.

Table 10.2 Segregation requirements of fire alarm and emergency lighting standards

Fire alarms BS 5839	**Emergency lighting** BS 5266
a installation in conduit, ducting, trunking or a channel reserved for fire alarms, or	**a** physical segregation by a minimum distance of 300 mm, or
b a mechanically strong, rigid and continuous partition of non-combustible material,	**b** use of mineral cables, or
c mounting at a distance of at least 300 mm from conductors of other systems, or	**c** use of cables to BS 6387 Cat B.
d wiring in cables complying with BS 7629, or	
e wiring in mineral insulated copper sheathed cable with an insulating sheath or barrier. The exposed-to-touch temperature rating of the IEE Wiring Regulations should not be exceeded.	

10.3 Site preparation and resistance to contaminants and moisture (Approved document C)

The requirement of Part C is shown below

Requirement	*Limits on application*
Site preparation and resistance to contaminants and moisture **Preparation of site and resistance to contaminants.** **C1** (1) The ground to be covered by the building shall be reasonably free from any material that might damage the building or affect its stability, including vegetable matter, topsoil and pre-existing foundations. (2) Reasonable precautions shall be taken to avoid danger to health and safety caused by contaminants on or in the ground covered, or to be covered by the building and any land associated with the building. (3) Adequate sub-soil drainage shall be provided if it is needed to avoid – (a) the passage of ground moisture to the interior of the building; (b) damage to the building, including damage through the transport of water-borne contaminants to the foundations of the building. (4) For the purpose of this requirement, "contaminant" means any substance which is or may become harmful to persons or buildings including substances which are corrosive, explosive, flammable, radioactive or toxic. **Resistance to moisture** C2. The floors, walls and roof of the building shall adequately protect the building and people who use the building from harmful effects caused by: (a) ground moisture; (b) precipitation and wind-driven spray; (c) interstitial and surface condensation.	

Persons carrying out electrical work in new buildings must cooperate with the main contractor in complying with the precautions necessary on the site. This will include:

- Sealing cable entries into the building to prevent the ingress of gas or water
- Taking care that no gas or water seals are penetrated.

10.4 Resistance to the passage of sound (Approved document E)

The requirement of Part E is shown below:

Requirement	*Limits on application*
Protection against sound from other parts of the building and adjoining buildings	
E1. Dwelling-houses, flats and rooms for residential purposes shall be designed and constructed in such a way that they provide reasonable resistance to sound from other parts of the same building and from adjoining buildings.	
Protection against sound within a dwelling-house etc.	
E2. Dwelling-houses, flats and rooms for residential purposes shall be designed and constructed in such a way that – (a) internal walls between a bedroom or a room containing a water closet, and other rooms; and (b) internal floors provide reasonable resistance to sound.	Requirement E2 does not apply to – (a) an internal wall which contains a door; (b) an internal wall which separates an en suite toilet from the associated bedroom; (c) existing walls and floors in a building which is subject to a material change of use.
Reverberation in the common internal parts of buildings containing flats or rooms for residential purposes	
E3. The common internal parts of buildings which contain flats or rooms for residential purposes shall be designed and constructed in such a way as to prevent more reverberation around the common parts than is reasonable.	Requirement E3 only applies to corridors, stairwells, hallways and entrance halls which give access to the flat or room for residential purposes.
Acoustic conditions in schools	
E4. (1) Each room or other space in a school building shall be designed and constructed in such a way that it has the acoustic conditions and the insulation against disturbance by noise appropriate to its intended use. (2) For the purposes of this Part – "school" has the same meaning as in section 4 of the Education Act 1996[4]; and "school building" means any building forming a school or part of a school.	

Electrical installations must not degrade the resistance to sound of the building. This may require the sealing of cable, conduit and trunking penetrations of walls and ceilings/floors. Trunking and conduit should not be so installed as to conduct sound in contravention of Part E above. The effects of thermal insulation are discussed in Section 10.6 of this Guide.

10.5 Ventilation (Approved document F)

Part F schedule 1 to the Building Regulations 1991 requires:

Requirement	*Limits on application*
Means of ventilation F1 There shall be adequate means of ventilation provided for people in the building.	Requirement F1 does not apply to a building or space within a building – a) into which people do not normally go; or b) which is used solely for storage; or c) which is a garage used solely in connection with a single dwelling.

Approved document F specifies requirements for the ventilation of domestic buildings, with particular requirements for kitchens, utility rooms and bathrooms as summarised in the Table overleaf.

The requirements are included in this Guide because work in a kitchen or bathroom subject to the Building Regulations might involve the installer (electrician) in the installation of extract fans of sufficient capacity.

Section 1 of Approved document F gives guidance on the following ways of providing adequate means of ventilation in domestic buildings:

- Mechanical extract ventilation operated manually and/or by a sensor or controller and combined with trickle ventilators; or
- Passive Stack Ventilation (PSV) operated manually and/or by a sensor or controller and combined with trickle ventilators; or
- An appropriate open-flued heating appliance used as an alternative to other forms of extract ventilation.

The guidance in Approved document F applies to all new dwellings and non-domestic buildings, and also to those formed by the change of use of other buildings.

Table 1: Ventilation of rooms containing openable windows (i.e. located on an external wall)			
Room[(6)]	**Rapid ventilation (e.g. opening windows)**	**Background ventilation**[(1)] (See diagram 1 in Approved document F)	**Extract ventilation fan rates or passive stack (PSV)** [(2,3)]
Habitable room	1/20th of floor area	8000 mm^2	-
Kitchen	Opening window (no minimum size)	4000 mm^2	30 litres/second adjacent to a hob, or 60 litres/second elsewhere[(4)] or PSV
Utility room[(5)]	Opening window (no minimum size)	4000 mm^2	30 litres/second or PSV
Bathroom with or without wc	Opening window (no minimum size)	4000 mm^2	15 litres/second or PSV
Sanitary accommodation (separate from bathroom)	1/20th of floor area, or mechanical extract at 6 litres/second	4000 mm^2	-

Notes:

1. As an alternative approach to the provision listed in Table 1, the overall provision for background ventilation for the dwelling should be equivalent to an average of 6000 mm^2 per room for rooms listed in Table 1, with a minimum provision of 4000 mm^2 in each room.

2. Passive stack ventilation provided in accordance with BRE Information paper 13/94 or with appropriate third party certification, such as a BBA certificate, would be satisfactory.

3. Open-flued appliances take their combustion air from the room or space in which they are installed and so contribute to the extract ventilation when in operation. They can also be arranged to provide adequate extract ventilation when not firing. For instance no additional extract ventilation would be necessary to satisfy the requirement if:

a. the solid fuel open-flued appliance is a primary source of heating, cooking or hot water production; or

b. the open-fued appliance has a flue with a free area at least equivalent to a 125 mm diameter duct and the appliance's combustion air inlet and dilution air inlet are permanently open, ie there is a path with no control dampers which could block the flow or the ventilation path can be left open when the appliance is not in use (see also paragraph 1.8 of Approved document F).

4. Mechanical extract ventilation should be rated:

a. not less than 30 litres/second, (i) when incorporated within a cooker hood or (ii) when located near the ceiling within 300 mm of the centreline of the space for the hob and under humidistat control; or

b. not less than 60 litres/second when located elsewhere.

5. For the purpose of the Building Regulations, provision for ventilation need not be made for a utility room which is accessible only from outside the building.

6. Where rooms serve a combined function as defined in Table 1, such as a kitchen-diner, the individual provisions for rapid, background and extract ventilation need not be duplicated provided that the greatest provision for the individual functions is made from Table 1.

10.6 Conservation of fuel and power (Approved document L1)

The requirement of Part L1 is shown below:

Requirement	*Limits on application*
Dwellings **L1.** Reasonable provision shall be made for the conservation of fuel and power in dwellings by –	
(a) limiting the heat loss: (i) through the fabric of the building; (ii) from hot water pipes and hot air ducts used for space heating; (iii) from hot water vessels;	
(b) providing space heating and hot water systems which are energy-efficient;	
(c) providing lighting systems with appropriate lamps and sufficient controls so that energy can be used efficiently; (d) providing sufficient information with the heating and hot water services so that building occupiers can operate and maintain the services in such a manner as to use no more energy than is reasonable in the circumstances.	The requirement for sufficient controls in requirement L1 (c) applies only to external lighting systems fixed to the building.

Approved document L1 requires reasonable provision to be made for the conservation of fuel and power in dwellings. Amongst other requirements is that lighting systems are provided with appropriate lamps and sufficient controls so that energy can be used efficiently.

10.6.1 Internal lighting

One way of complying with the requirements of Part L1 of the Building Regulations, for internal lighting, is to provide fixed lighting points that can only take lamps having a luminous efficacy greater than 40 lumens per circuit-watt. Such lighting points should be provided at a reasonable number of locations where lighting can be expected to have the most use.

Examples of lamps that achieve this efficacy requirement include fluorescent tubes and Compact Fluorescent Lamps (CFLs).

Table 10.6 Method for determining the number of locations to be equipped as a reasonable provision for efficient lighting

Number of rooms created[1]	Recommended minimum number of locations[2]
1 - 3	1
4 - 6	2
7 - 9	3
10 - 12	4

Notes:
1. Hall, stairs and landing(s) count as one room (but may contain more than one fitting)
2. Excludes garages, lofts and outhouses

10.6.2 External lighting fixed to the building

External lighting includes lighting in porches, but not lighting in garages or carports. When providing external lighting, reasonable provision should be made to enable effective control and/or the use of efficient lamps. A way of showing compliance when providing external lighting would be to install systems that:

(a) automatically extinguish when there is enough daylight, and when not required at night; and/or
(b) have lamp holders that can only be used with lamps having an efficacy greater than 40 lumens per circuit-watt (such as fluorescent or compact fluorescent lamp types).

10.6.3 Thermal insulation

Care must be taken with the design and installation of electrical installations in dwellings with high levels of thermal insulation. Circuits designed for cable installation methods 1, 3 and 6 (see 2.3.1 and 4.1) must not be totally enclosed in thermal insulation. The builder must be made aware of the electrical installation thermal design limitations, that is the need to keep cables in contact with a thermally conductive surface on one side.

10.7 Access and facilities for the disabled (Approved document M)

The requirement of Part M is shown below:

Requirement	*Limits on application*
PART M ACCESS TO AND USE OF BUILDINGS	
Access and Use	The requirements of this Part do not apply to–
M1. Reasonable provision shall be made for people to–	
(a) gain access to; and	(a) an extension of or material alteration of a dwelling; or
(b) use the building and its facilities.	(b) any part of a building which is used solely to enable the building or any service or fitting in the building to be inspected, repaired or maintained.
Access to Extensions to Buildings and other Dwellings	
M2. Suitable independent access shall be provided to the extension where reasonably practicable.	Requirement M2 does not apply where suitable access to the extension is provided through the building that is extended.
Sanitary Conveniences in Extensions to Buildings other than Dwellings	
M3. If sanitary conveniences are provided in any building that is to be extended, reasonable provision shall be made within the extension for sanitary conveniences.	Requirement M3 does not apply where there is reasonable provision for sanitary conveniences elsewhere in the building, such that people occupied in, or otherwise having occasion to enter the extension, can gain access to and use those sanitary conveniences.
Sanitary Conveniences in Dwellings	
M4. (1) Reasonable provision shall be made in the entrance storey for sanitary conveniences, or where the entrance storey contains no habitable rooms, reasonable provision for sanitary conveniences shall be made in either the entrance storey or principal storey.	
(2) In this paragraph "entrance storey" means storey which contains the principal entrance and "principal storey" means the storey nearest the entrance storey which contains a habitable room, or if there are two such storeys equally near, either such storey.	

Part M of schedule 1 includes in its requirements that reasonable provision must be made for disabled people to gain access to and use a building.

Heights of switches and sockets-outlets

The Building Regulations require switches and socket-outlets in dwellings to be installed so that all persons including those whose reach is limited can easily use them. A way of satisfying the requirement is to install switches and socket-outlets in habitable rooms at a height of between 450 mm and 1200 mm from the finished floor level – see Figure 10.7. Unless the dwelling is for persons whose reach is limited the requirements would not apply to kitchens and garages but specifically only to rooms that visitors would normally use.

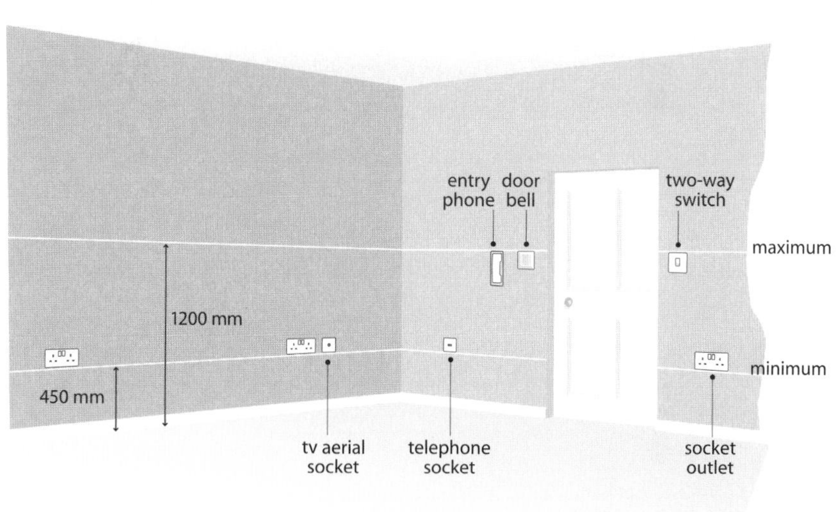

▲ **Figure 10.7** Height of switches, socket-outlets etc

The guidance given in Approved document M applies to all new dwellings. Note that if a dwelling is rewired there is no requirement to provide the measures described above providing that upon completion the building is no worse in terms of the level of compliance with the other Parts of Schedule 1 to the Building Regulations.

Identification of conductors 11

- **Introduction**
- **Alteration or addition to an existing installation**
- **Switch wires**
- **Intermediate and two-way switch wires**
- **Phase conductors in a new installation**
- **Changes to cable core colour identification**
- **Alteration or addition to a d.c. installation**

11.1. Introduction

The requirements of BS 7671 have been harmonised with the technical intent of CENELEC Standard HD 384.5.514: Identification, including 514.3: Identification of conductors.

The cable standards have been harmonised with CENELEC Harmonisation Document HD 308 S2: 2001 Identification of cores in cables and flexible cords. These standards specify the cable core marking including cable core colours to be implemented in the CENELEC countries.

This Chapter provides guidance on marking at the interface between old and harmonised colours, and general guidance on the colours to be used for conductors.

British Standards for fixed and flexible cables have been harmonised with the colours in HD 308 S2. BS 7671 has been modified to align with these cable colours, but also allows other suitable methods of marking connections by colours (tapes, sleeves or discs), or by alphanumerics (letters and/or numbers). Methods may be mixed within an installation.

Installations commencing on-site after 31 March 2004 and before 1 April 2006 may use the new harmonised identification or the old, but not both. Installations commencing on-site after 1 April 2006 must use harmonised identification.

Table 11a Identification of conductors

Function	Alphanumeric	Colour
Protective conductors		Green-and-yellow
Functional earthing conductor		Cream
a.c. power circuit[1]		
Phase of single-phase circuit	L	Brown
Neutral of single- or three-phase circuit	N	Blue
Phase 1 of three-phase a.c. circuit	L1	Brown
Phase 2 of three-phase a.c. circuit	L2	Black
Phase 3 of three-phase a.c. circuit	L3	Grey
Two-wire unearthed d.c. power circuit		
Positive of two-wire circuit	L+	Brown
Negative of two-wire circuit	L-	Grey
Two-wire earthed d.c. power circuit		
Positive (of negative earthed) circuit	L+	Brown
Negative (of negative earthed) circuit[2]	M	Blue
Positive (of positive earthed) circuit[2]	M	Blue
Negative (of positive earthed) circuit	L-	Grey
Three-wire d.c. power circuit		
Outer positive of two-wire circuit derived from three-wire system	L+	Brown
Outer negative of two-wire circuit derived from three-wire system	L-	Grey
Positive of three-wire circuit	L+	Brown
Mid-wire of three-wire circuit[2][3]	M	Blue
Negative of three-wire circuit	L-	Grey
Control circuits, ELV and other applications		
Phase conductor	L	Brown, Black, Red, Orange, Yellow, Violet, Grey, White, Pink or Turquoise
Neutral or mid-wire[4]	N or M	Blue

NOTES:

[1] Power circuits include lighting circuits.

[2] M identifies either the mid-wire of a three-wire d.c. circuit, or the earthed conductor of a two-wire earthed d.c. circuit.

[3] Only the middle wire of three-wire circuits may be earthed.

[4] An earthed PELV conductor is blue.

11.2. Alteration or addition to an existing installation

11.2.1 Single-phase

An alteration or an addition made to a single-phase installation need not be marked at the interface provided that:

(i) the old cables are correctly identified by the colour red for phase and black for neutral, and
(ii) the new cables are correctly identified by the colour brown for phase and blue for neutral.

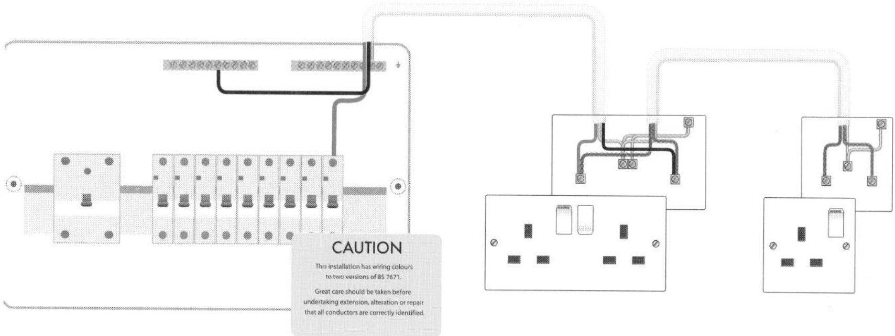

▲ **Figure 11.2.1** Extension to a single-phase installation

A warning label must be provided at the consumer unit or distribution board.

11.2.2 Two- or three-phase installation

Where an alteration or an addition is made to a two- or a three-phase installation wired in the old core colours with cable to the new core colours, unambiguous identification is required at the interface. Cores should be marked as follows:

- Neutral conductors: old and new conductors: N
- Phase conductors: old and new conductors: L1, L2, L3.

Table 11b Example of conductor marking at the interface for additions and alterations to an a.c. installation identified with the old cable colours

Function	Old conductor		New conductor	
	Colour	**Marking**	**Marking**	**Colour**
Phase 1 of a.c.	Red	L1	L1	Brown[(1)]
Phase 2 of a.c.	Yellow	L2	L2	Black[(1)]
Phase 3 of a.c.	Blue	L3	L3	Grey[(1)]
Neutral of a.c.	Black	N	N	Blue
Protective conductor	Green-and-Yellow			Green-and-Yellow

[(1)]Three single-core cables with insulation of the same colour may be used if identified at the terminations.

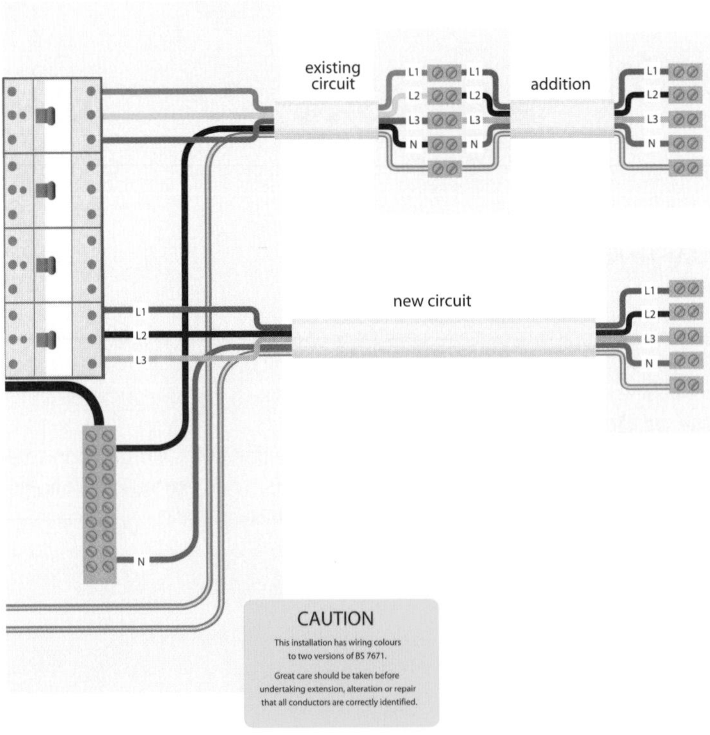

▲ **Figure 11.2.2** Addition to a three-phase installation

11.3. Switch wires in a new installation or an alteration or addition to an existing installation

Where a two-core cable with cores coloured brown and blue is used as a switch wire, both conductors being phase conductors, the blue conductor must be marked brown or L at its terminations.

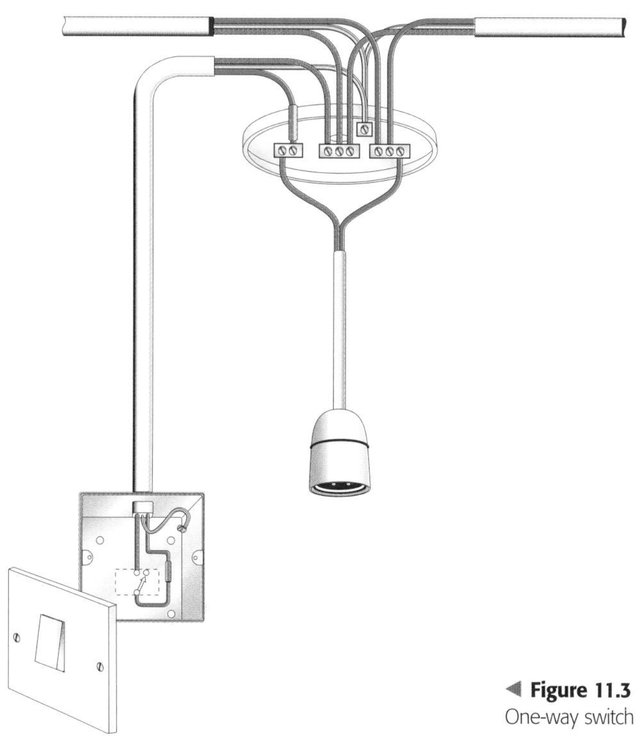

Figure 11.3
One-way switch

11.4. Intermediate and two-way switch wires in a new installation or an alteration or addition to an existing installation

Where a three-core cable with cores coloured brown, black and grey is used as a switch wire, all three conductors being phase conductors, the black and grey conductors must be marked brown or L at their terminations.

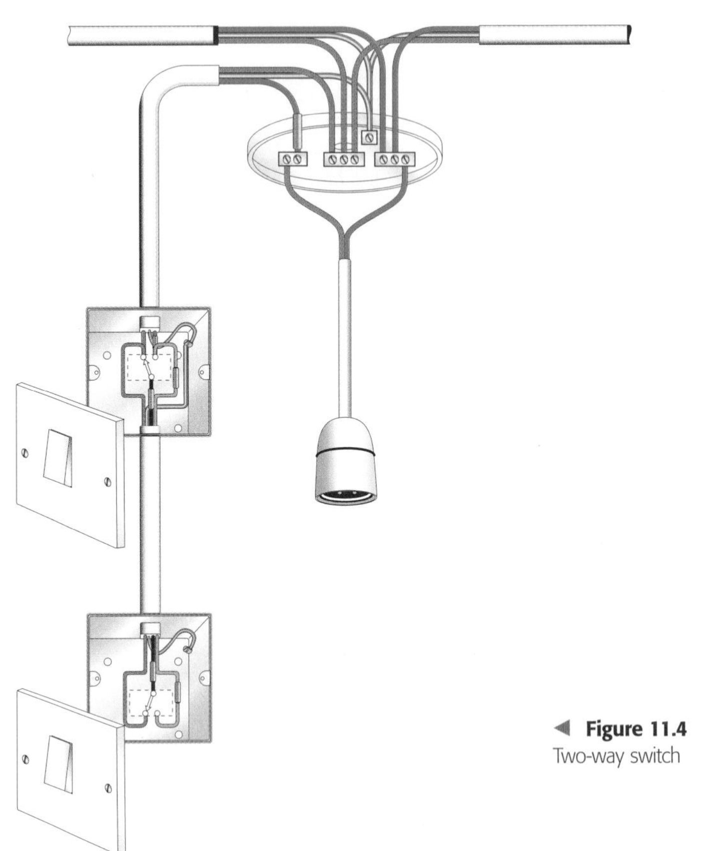

Figure 11.4
Two-way switch

11.5. Phase conductors in a new installation or an alteration or addition to an existing installation

Phase conductors should be coloured as shown in Table 11a.
Other permitted colours for phase conductors are brown, black, red, orange, yellow, violet, grey, white, pink or turquoise.

In a two- or three-phase power circuit the phase conductors may all be of one of the permitted colours and either identified L1, L2, L3 or marked brown, black, grey at their terminations to identify the phases.

11.6. Changes to cable core colour identification

Table 11c Cable to BS 6004 (flat cable with bare cpc)

Cable type	Old core colours	New core colours
Single-core + bare cpc	Red or Black	Brown or Blue
Two-core + bare cpc	Red, Black	Brown, Blue
Alt. two-core + bare cpc	Red, Red	Brown, Brown
Three-core + bare cpc	Red, Yellow, Blue	Brown, Black, Grey

Table 11d Standard 600/1000 V armoured cable BS 6346, BS 5467 or BS 6724

Cable type	Old core colours	New core colours
Single-core	Red or Black	Brown or Blue
Two-core	Red, Black	Brown, Blue
Three-core	Red, Yellow, Blue	Brown, Black, Grey
Four-core	Red, Yellow, Blue, Black	Brown, Black, Grey, Blue
Five-core	Red, Yellow, Blue, Black, Green-and-Yellow	Brown, Black, Grey, Blue, Green-and-Yellow

Table 11e Flexible cable to BS 6500

Cable type	Old core colours	New core colours
Two-core	Brown, Blue	No change
Three-core	Brown, Blue, Green-and-Yellow	No change
Four-core	Black, Blue, Brown, Green-and-Yellow	Brown, Black, Grey, Green-and-Yellow
Five-core	Black, Blue, Brown, Black, Green-and-Yellow	Brown, Black, Grey, Blue, Green-and-Yellow

11.7. Alteration or addition to a d.c. installation

When an alteration or an addition is made to a d.c. installation wired in the old core colours with cable to the new core colours, unambiguous identification is required at the interface. Cores must be marked as follows:

Neutral and mid-point conductors
Old and new conductors: M

Phase conductors
Old and new conductors: Brown or Grey, or
old and new conductors: L, L+ or L−.

Table 11f Example of conductor marking at the interface for additions and alterations to a d.c. installation identified with the old cable colour

Function	Old conductor colour	Old conductor marking	New conductor marking	New conductor colour
Two-wire unearthed d.c. power circuit				
Positive of two-wire circuit	Red	L+	L+	Brown
Negative of two-wire circuit	Black	L−	L−	Grey
Two-wire earthed d.c. power circuit				
Positive (of negative earthed) circuit	Red	L+	L+	Brown
Negative (of negative earthed) circuit	Black	M	M	Blue
Positive (of positive earthed) circuit	Black	M	M	Blue
Negative (of positive earthed) circuit	Blue	L−	L−	Grey
Three-wire d.c. power circuit				
Outer positive of two-wire circuit derived from three-wire system	Red	L+	L+	Brown
Outer negative of two-wire circuit derived from three-wire system	Red	L−	L−	Grey
Positive of three-wire circuit	Red	L+	L+	Brown
Mid-wire of three-wire circuit	Black	M	M	Blue
Negative of three-wire circuit	Blue	L−	L−	Grey

Appendix A

Part I of BS 7671

A

Appendix A is a reproduction of Part 1 of BS 7671: Requirements for Electrical Installations (The IEE Wiring Regulations – Sixteenth Edition).

PART 1
SCOPE, OBJECT AND FUNDAMENTAL PRINCIPLES

CHAPTER 11
SCOPE

110-01 General

110-01-01 The Regulations apply to electrical installations such as those of:
(i) residential premises
(ii) commercial premises
(iii) public premises
(iv) industrial premises
(v) agricultural and horticultural premises
(vi) prefabricated buildings
(vii) caravans, caravan parks and similar sites
(viii) construction sites, exhibitions, fairs and other installations in temporary buildings
(ix) highway power supplies and street furniture, and outdoor lighting.

The Regulations include requirements for:
(x) circuits supplied at nominal voltages up to and including 1000 V a.c. or 1500 V d.c. For a.c., the preferred frequencies which are taken into account in this standard (BS 7671) are 50 Hz, 60 Hz and 400 Hz. The use of other frequencies for special purposes is not excluded
(xi) circuits, other than the internal wiring of apparatus, operating at voltages exceeding 1000 V and derived from an installation having a voltage not exceeding 1000 V a.c., e.g. discharge lighting, electrostatic precipitators
(xii) any wiring systems and cables not specifically covered by an appliance standard
(xiii) all consumer installations external to buildings

(xiv) fixed wiring for communication and information technology, signalling, control and the like (excluding internal wiring of apparatus)
(xv) the addition to or alteration of installations and also parts of existing installations affected by the addition or alteration.

The Regulations are intended to be applied to electrical installations generally but, in certain cases, they may need to be supplemented by the requirements or recommendations of other British Standards or by the requirements of the person ordering the work.

Such cases include the following:

(xvi) electric signs and high voltage luminous discharge tube installations – BS 559
(xvii) emergency lighting – BS 5266
(xviii) electrical apparatus for explosive gas atmospheres – BS EN 60079 and BS EN 50014
(xix) electrical apparatus for use in the presence of combustible dust – BS EN 50281
(xx) fire detection and alarm systems in buildings – BS 5839
(xxi) installations subject to the Telecommunications Act 1984 – BS 6701 Part 1
(xxii) electric surface heating systems – BS 6351
(xxiii) electrical installations for open cast mines and quarries – BS 6907.

110-02 Exclusions from scope
110-02-01 The Regulations do not apply to the following installations:

(i) 'distributors equipment' as defined in the Electricity Safety, Quality and Continuity Regulations 2002
(ii) railway traction equipment, rolling stock and signalling equipment
(iii) equipment of motor vehicles, except those to which the requirements of the Regulations concerning caravans are applicable
(iv) equipment on board ships
(v) equipment of mobile and fixed offshore installations
(vi) equipment of aircraft
(vii) those aspects of mines and quarries specifically covered by Statutory Regulations
(viii) radio interference suppression equipment, except so far as it affects safety of the electrical installation
(ix) lightning protection of buildings covered by BS 6651
(x) those aspects of lift installations covered by BS 5655.

110-03 Equipment
110-03-01 The Regulations apply to items of electrical equipment only so far as selection and application of the equipment in the installation are concerned. The Regulations do not deal with requirements for the construction of assemblies of electrical equipment, which are required to comply with appropriate standards.

110-04 Relationship with Statutory Regulations

110-04-01 The Regulations are non-statutory regulations. They may, however, be used in a court of law in evidence to claim compliance with a statutory requirement. The relevant statutory provisions are listed in Appendix 2 (of BS 7671) and include Acts of Parliament and Regulations made thereunder. In some cases Regulations may be accompanied by Codes of Practice approved under Section 16 of the Health and Safety at Work etc. Act 1974. The legal status of these Codes is explained in Section 17 of the 1974 Act.

For a supply given in accordance with the Electricity Safety, Quality and Regulations 2002, it shall be deemed that the connection with earth of the neutral of the supply is permanent. Outside Great Britain, confirmation shall be sought from the distributor that the supply conforms to requirements corresponding to those of the Electricity Safety, Quality and Regulations 2002, in this respect.

110-05 Installations in premises subject to licensing

110-05-01 For installations in premises over which a licensing or other authority exercises a statutory control, the requirements of that authority shall be ascertained and complied with in the design and execution of the installation.

CHAPTER 12
OBJECT AND EFFECTS

120-01 General

120-01-01 This standard contains the rules for the design and erection of electrical installations so as to provide for safety and proper functioning for the intended use.

120-01-02 Chapter 13 of this standard states the fundamental principles. It does not include detailed technical requirements which may be subject to modifications because of technical developments.

120-01-03 This standard sets out technical requirements intended to ensure that electrical installations conform to the fundamental principles of Chapter 13, as follows:

Part 3 – Assessment of general characteristics

Part 4 – Protection for safety

Part 5 – Selection and erection of equipment

Part 6 – Special installations or locations

Part 7 – Inspection and testing.

Any intended departure from these Parts requires special consideration by the designer of the installation and shall be noted on the Electrical Installation Certificate specified in Part 7.

120-02 New materials and inventions

120-02-01 Where the use of a new material or invention leads to departures from the Regulations, the resulting degree of safety of the installation is to be not less than that obtained by compliance with the Regulations. Such use is to be noted on the Electrical Installation Certificate specified in Part 7.

CHAPTER 13
FUNDAMENTAL PRINCIPLES

130 PROTECTION FOR SAFETY
130-01 General

130-01-01 The requirements of this section are intended to provide for the safety of persons, livestock and property against dangers and damage which may arise in the reasonable use of electrical installations.

In electrical installations, risk of injury may result from:

(i) shock currents

(ii) excessive temperatures likely to cause burns, fires and other injurious effects

(iii) mechanical movement of electrically actuated equipment, in so far as such injury is intended to be prevented by electrical emergency switching or by electrical switching for mechanical maintenance of non-electrical parts of such equipment

(iv) explosion.

130-02 Protection against electric shock

Protection against direct contact (normal conditions)

130-02-01 Persons and livestock shall be protected so far as is reasonably practicable against dangers that may arise from contact with live parts of the installation.

This protection can be achieved by one of the following methods:

(i) preventing a current from passing through the body of any person or any livestock
(ii) limiting the current which can pass through a body to a value lower than the shock current.

Protection against indirect contact (under single fault conditions)

130-02-02 Persons and livestock shall be protected against dangers that may arise from contact with exposed-conductive-parts during a fault.

This protection can be achieved by one of the following methods:

(i) preventing current passing through the body of any person or any livestock

(ii) limiting the fault current which can pass through a body to a value lower than the shock current
(iii) automatic disconnection of the supply in a determined time on the occurrence of a fault likely to cause a current to flow through a body in contact with exposed-conductive-parts, where the value of that current is equal to or greater than the shock current.

In connection with the protection against indirect contact, the application of the method of equipotential bonding is one of the important principles for safety.

130-03 Protection against thermal effects
130-03-01 So far as is reasonably practicable the electrical installation shall be so arranged that the risk of ignition of flammable materials due to high temperature or electric arc is reduced. In addition, during normal operation of the electrical equipment, the risk of burns to persons or livestock shall be reduced so far as is reasonably practicable.

130-03-02 Persons, fixed equipment and fixed materials adjacent to electrical equipment shall be protected against harmful effects of heat or thermal radiation emitted by electrical equipment, particularly the following consequences:

(i) combustion, ignition, or degradation of materials
(ii) risk of burns
(iii) impairment of the safe function of installed equipment.

Electrical equipment shall not present a fire hazard to adjacent materials.

Protection against overcurrent
130-04-01 So far as is reasonably practicable, persons or livestock shall be protected against injury and property shall be protected against damage due to excessive temperatures or electromechanical stresses caused by any overcurrents likely to arise in live conductors.

130-05 Protection against fault current
130-05-01 Conductors, and any other parts likely to carry a fault current, shall be capable of carrying that current without attaining an excessive temperature.

For live conductors, compliance with Regulation 130-04 assures their protection against overcurrents caused by faults.

130-06 Protection against overvoltage
130-06-01 So far as is reasonably practicable, persons or livestock shall be protected against injury and property shall be protected against any harmful effects as a consequence of a fault between live parts of circuits supplied at different voltages.

130-06-02 So far as is reasonably practicable, persons, livestock and property shall be protected against the consequence of overvoltages likely to arise due to atmospheric phenomena and switching.

130-07 Additions and alterations to an installation

130-07-01 No addition or alteration, temporary or permanent, shall be made to an existing installation, unless it has been ascertained that the rating and the condition of any existing equipment, including that of the distributor, which will have to carry any additional load is adequate for the altered circumstances and the earthing and bonding arrangements are also adequate.

131 DESIGN

131-01 General

131-01-01 The electrical installation shall be designed to provide for:
(i) the protection of persons, livestock and property in accordance with Section 130
(ii) the proper functioning of the electrical installation for the intended use.

The information required as a basis for design is listed in Regulations 131-02 to 131-05. The requirements with which the design shall comply are stated in Regulations 131-06 to 131-14.

131-02 Characteristics of available supply or supplies

131-02-01 Information on the characteristics of the available supply or supplies as below shall be determined by calculation, measurement, enquiry, or inspection:

(i) Nature of current: a.c. and/or d.c.

(ii) Purpose and number of conductors:
- for a.c. phase conductor(s)
  neutral conductor
  protective conductor
  PEN conductor
- for d.c. conductors equivalent to those listed above (outer/middle/earthed live conductors, protective conductor, PEN conductor)

(iii) Values and tolerances:
- nominal voltage and voltage tolerances
- nominal frequency and frequency tolerances
- maximum current allowable
- prospective short-circuit current
- earth fault loop impedance

(iv) Protective measures inherent in the supply, e.g. earthed neutral or mid-wire

(v) Particular requirements of the distributor.

131-03 Nature of demand

131-03-01 The number and type of circuits required for lighting, heating, power, control, signalling, communication and information technology, etc shall be determined from knowledge of:

(i) location of points of power demand
(ii) loads to be expected on the various circuits
(iii) daily and yearly variation of demand
(iv) any special conditions
(v) requirements for control, signalling, communication and information technology, etc.

131-04 Emergency supply or supplies for safety services

131-04-01 Where a supply for safety services is specified the following shall be determined:
(i) characteristics of the supply
(ii) circuits to be supplied by the safety source.

131-05 Environmental conditions

131-05-01 Equipment likely to be exposed to weather, corrosive atmospheres or other adverse conditions, shall be so constructed or protected as may be necessary to prevent danger arising from such exposure.

131-05-02 Equipment in surroundings susceptible to risk of fire or explosion shall be so constructed or protected and such other special precautions shall be taken to prevent, so far as is reasonably practicable, danger.

131-06 Cross-sectional area of conductors

131-06-01 The cross-sectional area of conductors shall be determined according to:
(i) the admissible maximum temperature
(ii) the voltage drop limit
(iii) the electromechanical stresses likely to occur due to short-circuit and earth fault currents
(iv) other mechanical stresses to which conductors are likely to be exposed
(v) the maximum impedance for operation of short-circuit and earth fault protection.

131-07 Type of wiring and method of installation

131-07-01 The choice of the type of wiring system and the method of installation shall include consideration of the following:

(i) the nature of the location
(ii) the nature of the structure supporting the wiring
(iii) accessibility of wiring to persons and livestock
(iv) voltage
(v) the electromechanical stresses likely to occur due to short-circuit and earth fault currents

(vi) other stresses (e.g. mechanical, thermal and those associated with fire) to which the wiring is likely to be exposed during the erection of the electrical installation or in service.

131-08 Protective equipment

131-08-01 The characteristics of protective equipment shall be determined with respect to their function including protection against the effects of:

(i) overcurrent (overload, short-circuit)
(ii) earth fault current
(iii) overvoltage
(iv) undervoltage and no-voltage.

The protective devices shall operate at values of current, voltage and time which are suitably related to the characteristics of the circuits and to the possibilities of danger.

131-09 Emergency control

131-09-01 Where in case of danger there is necessity for immediate interruption of supply, an interrupting device shall be installed in such a way that it can be easily recognised and effectively and rapidly operated.

131-10 Disconnecting devices

131-10-01 Disconnecting devices shall be provided so as to permit disconnection of the electrical installation, circuits or individual items of apparatus as required for maintenance, testing, fault detection and repair.

131-11 Prevention of mutual detrimental influence

131-11-01 The electrical installation shall be arranged in such a way that no mutual detrimental influence will occur between different electrical installations and non-electrical installations of the building. Electromagnetic interference shall be taken into account.

131-12 Accessibility of electrical equipment

131-12-01 Electrical equipment shall be arranged so as to afford as may be necessary:

(i) sufficient space for the initial installation and later replacement of individual items
(ii) accessibility for operation, inspection, testing, maintenance and repair.

131-13 Protective devices and switches

131-13-01 A single-pole fuse, switch or circuit-breaker shall be inserted in the phase conductor only.

131-13-02 No switch or circuit-breaker, except where linked, or fuse shall be inserted in an earthed neutral conductor and any linked switch or linked circuit-breaker inserted in an earthed neutral conductor shall be arranged to break all the related phase conductors.

131-14 Isolation and switching

131-14-01 Effective means, suitably placed for ready operation, shall be provided so that all voltage may be cut off from every installation, from every circuit thereof and from all equipment, as may be necessary to prevent or remove danger.

131-14-02 Every fixed electric motor shall be provided with an efficient means of switching off, readily accessible, easily operated and so placed as to prevent danger.

132 SELECTION OF ELECTRICAL EQUIPMENT

132-01 General

132-01-01 Every item of equipment shall comply with the appropriate EN or HD or National Standard implementing the HD. In the absence of an EN or HD, the equipment shall comply with the appropriate National Standard. In all other cases, reference shall be made to the appropriate IEC Standard or to an appropriate National Standard of another country.

132-01-02 Where there is no applicable standard, the item of equipment concerned shall be selected by special agreement between the person specifying the installation and the installer.

Voltage

132-01-03 The rated voltage of electrical equipment shall be suitable for the nominal voltage. Such equipment shall be suitable for the overvoltage category envisaged. For certain equipment as appropriate the lowest voltage likely to occur shall be taken into account.

Current

132-01-04 Electrical equipment shall be selected with respect to the maximum steady current (rms value for a.c.) which it has to carry in normal service, and with respect to the current likely to be carried in abnormal conditions and the period (e.g. operating time of protective devices if any) during which it may be expected to flow.

Frequency

132-01-05 Equipment shall be suitable for the frequencies likely to occur in the circuit.

Power

132-01-06 Electrical equipment which is selected on the basis of its power characteristics shall be suitable for the duty demanded of the equipment, taking into account the load factor and the normal service conditions.

Conditions of installation

132-01-07 Electrical equipment shall be selected so as to withstand safely the stresses, the environmental conditions (see Regulation 131-05) and the characteristics of its location. An item of equipment which does not by design have the properties corresponding to its location may be used where additional protection is provided.

Prevention of harmful effects

132-01-08 Electrical equipment shall be selected so that it will not cause, so far as is reasonably practicable, harmful effects on other equipment or impair the supply during normal service including switching operations.

133 ERECTION, VERIFICATION, AND PERIODIC INSPECTION AND TESTING OF ELECTRICAL INSTALLATIONS

133-01 Erection

133-01-01 Good workmanship and proper materials shall be used.

133-01-02 The characteristics of the electrical equipment, as determined in accordance with Section 132, shall not be impaired by the process of erection.

133-01-03 Conductors shall be identified in accordance with Section 514.

133-01-04 Every electrical joint and connection shall be of proper construction as regards conductance, insulation, mechanical strength and protection.

133-01-05 Electrical equipment shall be installed in such a manner that the design temperatures are not exceeded.

133-01-06 Electrical equipment likely to cause high temperatures or electric arcs shall be placed or guarded so as to minimise the risk of ignition of flammable materials.

Where the temperature of an exposed part of electrical equipment is likely to cause injury to persons or livestock that part shall be so located or guarded as to prevent accidental contact therewith.

133-02 Verification

133-02-01 On completion of an installation or an addition or alteration to an installation, appropriate inspection and testing shall be carried out to verify so far as is reasonably practicable that the requirements of this standard have been met.

133-03 Periodic inspection and testing

133-03-01 The person carrying out inspection and testing shall make a recommendation for subsequent periodic inspection and testing as detailed in Chapter 73 (of BS 7671).

Appendix B

British Standards

B

- Cables
- Accessories
- Switchgear
- Conduit and trunking
- Other equipment
- System standards

B1 Cables

BS 4553	Specification for 600/1000 V single-phase split concentric electric cables.
BS 4553-1: 1998	Cables having PVC insulation.
BS 4553-2: 1998	Cables having thermosetting insulation.
BS 4553-3: 1998	Cables having thermosetting insulation and low emission of smoke and corrosive gases when affected by fire.
BS 5467: 1997	Specification for 600/1000 V and 1900/3300 V armoured electric cables having thermosetting insulation.
BS 5593: 1978 (1991)	Specification for impregnated paper insulated cables with aluminium sheath/neutral conductor and three shaped solid aluminium phase conductors (CONSAC), 600/1000 V, for electricity supply.
BS 6004: 2000	Electric cables. PVC insulated, non-armoured cables for voltages up to and including 450/750 V, for electric power, lighting and internal wiring. (*PVC insulated and sheathed flat cable with protective conductor to Table 8.*)
BS 6141: 1991	Specification for insulated cables and flexible cords for use in high temperature zones.
BS 6207	Mineral insulated cables with a rated voltage not exceeding 750 V.
BS 6207-1: 1995	Cables.

BS 6207-2: 1995	Terminations.
BS 6346: 1997	Specification for 600/1000 V and 1900/3000 V armoured cables having pvc insulation.
BS 6500: 2000	Electric cables. Flexible cords rated up to 300/500 V, for use with appliances and equipment intended for domestic, office and similar environments.
BS 6724: 1997	Specification for 600/1000 V and 1900/3300 V armoured cables having thermosetting insulation and low emission of smoke and corrosive gases when affected by fire.
BS 6883: 1999	Elastomer insulated cables for fixed wiring in ships and on mobile and fixed offshore units. Requirements and test methods.
BS 7211: 1998	Specification for thermosetting insulated cables (non-armoured) for electric power and lighting with low emission of smoke and corrosive gases when affected by fire.
BS 7629-1: 1997	Specification for 300/500 V fire-resistant electric cables having low emission of smoke and corrosive gases when affected by fire. Multicore cables.
BS 7697: 1993	Nominal voltages for low voltage public electricity supply systems.
BS 7846: 2000	Electric cables. 600/1000 V armoured fire resistant electric cables having thermosetting insulation and low emission of smoke and corrosive gases when affected by fire.
BS 7889: 1997	Specification for 600/1000 V single-core unarmoured electric cables having thermosetting insulation.
BS 7919: 2001	Electric cables. Flexible cables rated up to 450/750 V, for use with appliances and equipment intended for industrial and similar environments.
BS 8436: 2004	300/500 V screened electric cables having low emission of smoke and corrosive gases when affected by fire, for use in thin partitions and building voids.
BS EN 60702-1: 2002	Mineral insulated cables and their terminations with a rated voltage not exceeding 750 V. Cables.

B2 Accessories

BS 67: 1987 (1999) Specification for ceiling roses.

BS 196: 1961 Specification for protected-type non-reversible plugs, socket-outlets, cable couplers and appliance couplers with earthing contacts for single-phase a.c. circuits up to 250 volts.

BS 546: 1950 (1988) Specification. Two-pole and earthing pin plugs, socket-outlets and socket-outlet adaptors.

BS 1362: 1973 (1992) Specification for general purpose fuse links for domestic and similar purposes (primarily for use in plugs).

BS 1363 13 A plugs, socket-outlets, connection units and adaptors.

BS 1363-1: 1995 Specification for rewirable and non-rewirable 13 A fused plugs.

BS 1363-2: 1995 Specification for 13 A switched and unswitched socket-outlets.

BS 1363-3: 1995 Specification for adaptors.

BS 1363-4: 1995 Specification for 13 A fused connection units: switched and unswitched.

BS 3676 Switches for household and similar fixed electrical installations.

BS 3676-1: 1989 Specification for general requirements. Now replaced by BS EN 60669-1: 2000, but remains current. BS EN 60669-1: 2000 is dual numbered BS 3676-1: 2000.

BS 4177: 1992 Specification for cooker control units.

BS 4491: 1969 Appliance couplers for household and similar general purposes.

BS 4573: 1970 (1979) Specification for 2-pin reversible plugs and shaver socket-outlets.

BS 4662: 1970 Specification for boxes for the enclosure of electrical accessories.

BS 5042: 1987 Specification for bayonet lampholders. Replaced by BS EN 61184: 1997.

BS 5518: 1977 (1999) Specification for electronic variable control switches (dimmer switches) for tungsten filament lighting.

BS 5733: 1995 Specification for general requirements for electrical accessories.

BS 6220: 1983	Specification for junction boxes for use in electrical installations with rated voltages not exceeding 250 V.
BS 6972: 1988	Specification for general requirements for luminaire supporting couplers for domestic, light industrial and commercial use.
BS 6991: 1990	Specification for 6/10 amp two pole weather-resistant couplers for household, commercial and light industrial equipment.
BS 7001: 1988	Specification for interchangeability and safety of a standardised luminaire supporting coupler. To be read in conjunction with BS 6972: 1988.
BS 7071: 1992 (1998)	Specification for portable residual current devices.
BS 7288: 1990 (1998)	Specification for socket-outlets incorporating residual current devices (SRCDs).
BS 7895: 1997	Specification for bayonet lampholders with enhanced safety.
BS EN 60238: 1999	Specification for Edison screw lampholders. Replaces BS EN 60238: (1996) (which remains current) and BS 6776: 1990.
BS EN 60309	Plugs, socket-outlets and couplers for industrial purposes. Replaces BS 4343: 1968.
BS EN 60309-1: 1999	General requirements. Replaces BS EN 60309-1: 1998 which remains current.
BS EN 60309-2: 1998	Dimensional interchangeability requirements for pin and contact-tube accessories of harmonized configurations (replaces BS 4343: 1992).
BS EN 60669	Switches for household and similar fixed electrical installations.
BS EN 60669-2-1: 2004	Particular requirements – Electronic switches.
BS EN 60669-2-2: 1998	Particular requirements – Remote control switches (RCS).
BS EN 60669-2-3: 1999	Particular requirements – Time delay switches (TDS).
BS EN 60669-2-4	Switches for household and similar fixed electrical installations Part 2-4: Particular requirements – Isolating switches.
BS EN 61184: 1997	Bayonet lampholders. Replaces BS 5042: 1987. Replaces BS EN 61184: 1995, which remains current.

B3 Switchgear

BS 88 Cartridge fuses for voltages up to and including 1000 V a.c. and 1500 V d.c.

BS 88-1: 1988 General requirements. Also numbered as BS EN 60269-1: 1994 and replaced by BS EN 60269-1: 1999, but remains current.

BS 88-2.1: 1988 Specification for fuses for use by authorized persons (mainly for industrial applications). Also numbered as BS EN 60269-2: 1995.

BS 88-6: 1988 (1992) Specification of supplementary requirements for fuses of compact dimensions for use in 240/415 V a.c. industrial and commercial electrical installations.

BS 646: 1958 (1991) Specification. Cartridge fuse links (rated up to 5 amperes) for a.c. and d.c. service.

BS 1361: 1971 (1986) Specification for cartridge fuses for a.c. circuits in domestic and similar premises.

BS 3036: 1958 (1992) Specification. Semi-enclosed electric fuses (rating up to 100 amperes and 240 volts to earth).

BS 3871 Specification for miniature and moulded case circuit-breakers. Miniature air-break circuit-breakers for a.c. circuits Replaced by BS EN 60898: 1991.

BS 4293: 1983 (1993) Specification for residual current operated circuit-breakers. (Replaced by BS EN 61008-1: 1995, BS EN 61008-2-1: 1995 and BS IEC 61008-2-2: 1990.)

BS 4343: 1992. Specification for industrial plugs, socket-outlets and couplers for a.c. and d.c. supplies Replaced by BS EN 60309 series.

BS 4363: 1998 Specification for distribution assemblies for electricity supplies for construction and building sites.

BS EN 60269 Low voltage fuses.

BS EN 60269-1: 1999 General requirements. Replaces BS EN 60269-1: 1994, which remains current and is also numbered as BS 88-1: 1988.

BS EN 60269-2: 1995 Supplementary requirements for fuses for use by authorized persons. Replaces BS 88-2.1: 1988.

BS EN 60439	Specification for low voltage switchgear and controlgear assemblies.
BS EN 60439-1: 1999	Specification for type-tested and partially type-tested assemblies.
BS EN 60439-2: 1993	Particular requirements for busbar trunking systems (busways). Formerly numbered as BS 5486: Part 2: 1988.
BS EN 60439-3: 1991	Specification for low-voltage switchgear and controlgear assemblies. Particular requirements for low-voltage switchgear and controlgear assemblies intended to be installed in places where unskilled persons have access to their use. Distribution Boards (UK consumer units).
BS EN 60439-4: 1991	Particular requirements for assemblies for construction sites (ACS).
BS EN 60898: 1991	Specification for circuit-breakers for overcurrent protection for household and similar installations. Replaces BS 3871 Part 1: 1965. Part 1: circuit breakers for a.c. operation.
BS EN 60947	Specification for low voltage switchgear and controlgear.
BS EN 60947-1: 1999	General rules.
BS EN 60947-2: 1996	Circuit-breakers. To be read in conjunction with BS EN 60947-1: 1992.
BS EN 60947-3: 1999	Switches, disconnectors, switch-disconnectors and fuse-combination units.
BS EN 60947-4:	Contactors and motor starters.
BS EN 60947-4-1: 1992	Electromechanical contactors and motor starters.
BS EN 61008	Residual current operated circuit-breakers without integral overcurrent protection for household and similar uses (RCCBs).
BS EN 61008-1: 1995	General rules. Replaces BS 4293: 1983 which remains current.
BS EN 61009	Residual current operated circuit-breakers with integral overcurrent protection for household and similar uses (RCBOs).
BS EN 61009-1: 1995	General rules.

B4 Conduit and trunking

BS 31: 1940 (1988)	Specification. Steel conduit and fittings for electrical wiring.
BS 731	Flexible steel conduit for cable protection and flexible steel tubing to enclose flexible drives.
BS 731-1: 1952 (1993)	Flexible steel conduit and adaptors for the protection of electric cables.
BS 4568	Specification for steel conduit and fittings with metric threads of ISO form for electrical installations.
BS 4568 Part 1: 1970 (1973)	Steel conduit, bends and couplers.
BS 4607	Non-metallic conduits and fittings for electrical installations.
BS 4678	Cable trunking.
BS 4678-1: 1971	Steel surface trunking.
BS 4678-2: 1973	Steel underfloor (duct) trunking.
BS 4678-4: 1982	Specification for cable trunking made of insulation material.
BS 6053: 1981 (1991)	Replaced by BS EN 60423: 1995.
BS 6099	Replaced by BS EN 50086. Specification for conduit systems for electrical installations.
BS EN 50085	Specification for cable trunking and ducting systems for electrical installations.
BS EN 50085-1: 1999	General requirements.
BS EN 50086	Specification for conduit systems for electrical installations.
BS EN 50086-1: 1994	General requirements.
BS EN 50086-2-1: 1996	Rigid conduit systems. Replaces BS 6099 Part 2 Section 2.2 : 1982 which remains current.
BS EN 60423: 1995	Conduits for electrical purposes. Outside diameters of conduits for electrical installations and threads for conduits.

B5 Other equipment

BS 559: 1998	Specification for electric signs and high voltage luminous discharge tube installations.
BS 951: 1999	Specification for clamps for earthing and bonding purposes.
BS 2754: 1976 (1999)	Memorandum. Construction of electrical equipment for protection against electric shock.
BS 2848: 1973	Specification for flexible insulating sleeving for electrical purposes. Note partially replaced by BS 6893: Part 3: 1987 and BS EN 60684-1: 1996.
BS 3535	Isolating transformers and safety isolating transformers. This standard is partially replaced by the BS EN 61558 series of standards, and these standards should be read jointly.
BS 3535-1: 1990	General requirements. (Also numbered as BS EN 60742: 1996.) Remains current only for use with BS 3535-2 and where application not covered by BS EN 61558 series.
BS 3535-2: 1990	Specification for transformers for reduced system voltage. To be read in conjunction with BS 3535-1.
BS 5655	Lifts and service lifts. BS 5655 is a multiple set of standards.
BS 5655-1: 1986 **BS 5655-2: 1988** **BS 5655-11: 1989**	BS 5655 -1, -2 and -11 are obsolescent and apply only to modernisation of existing installations. Replaced partly by BS EN 81-2: 1998 pending implementation of the EU Lift Directive.
BS 5839-4: 1988	Specification for control and indicating equipment, remains current but is replaced by BS EN 54-2: 1998 and BS EN 54-4: 1988.
BS EN 60335-2-35	Electric showers and instantaneous water heaters.
BS EN 60335-2-41	Pumps for showers.
BS EN 60335-2-53: 1997	Electric sauna heating appliances.
BS EN 60570: 1997	Electrical supply track systems for luminaires. Replaces BS 4533: Section 102.57: 1990.
BS EN 60598	Luminaires. Partly replaces BS 4533.
BS EN 60598-2-24: (1999)	Luminaires with limited surface temperature.

BS EN 60742: 1996	Isolating transformers and safety isolating transformers. Requirements. Replaces BS 3535, which remains current for use with Part 2. In turn, this document is also being partially replaced by documents in the BS EN 61558 series.
BS EN 61011: 1993	Electric fence energizers. Safety requirements for mains operated electric fence energizers. Replaces BS 2632: 1980. Replaced by BS EN 60335-2-76: 1999, but remains current.
BS EN 61011-1: 1993	Electric fence energizers. Safety requirements for battery operated electric fence energizers suitable for connection to the supply mains. Replaces BS 6369: 1983 To be read in conjunction with BS EN 61011: 1993. Replaced by BS EN 60335-2-76: 1999, but remains current.
BS EN 61558	Safety of power transformers, power supply units and similar. In view of the changes made to this series of standards, it is necessary to read these in conjunction with BS 3535-1: 1996 and BS 3535-2: 1990.
BS EN 61558-2-1: 1998	General requirements and tests. Partially replaces dual numbered standard BS EN 60742: 1996, BS 3535-1: 1996 and BS 3535-2: 1990.
BS EN 61558-2-2: 1998	Particular requirements for separating transformers for general use. Partially replaces dual numbered standard BS EN 60742: 1996, BS 3535-1: 1996 and BS 3535-2: 1990.
BS EN 61558-2-4: 1998	Particular requirements for isolating transformers for general use.
BS EN 61558-2-5: 1998	Particular requirements for shaver transformers and shaver units.
BS EN 61558-2-6	Particular requirements for safety isolating transformers for general use.
BS EN 61558-2-8: 1999	Particular requirements for bell and chime transformers.
BS EN 61558-2-17: 1998	Particular requirements for switch mode power supplies.

B6 System standards

BS 476	Fire tests on building materials and structure.
BS 476-4: 1970 (1984)	Non-combustibility test for materials.
BS 476 Part 5: 1979	Method of test for ignitability, now withdrawn.

BS 476-12: 1991	Method of test for ignitability also refers but methods of test are not identical.
BS 476-23: 1987	Methods for determination of the contribution of components to the fire resistance of a structure.
BS 4066	Tests on electric cables under fire conditions. Part 1: 1980 (1995) Method of test on a single insulated vertical wire or cable. Replaced by BS EN 50265-1: 1999.
BS 4066-3: 1994	Tests on bunched wires or cables.
BS 4444: 1989 (1995)	Guide to electrical earth monitoring and protective conductor proving.
BS 4727	Glossary of electrotechnical, power, telecommunications, electronics, lighting and colour terms.
BS 5266	Emergency lighting.
BS 5345	Replaced in part by BS EN 60079 Electrical apparatus for explosive gas atmospheres and BS EN 50014: 1998 Electrical apparatus for potentially explosive atmospheres. General requirements.
BS 5839	Fire detection and alarm systems for buildings.
BS 6351	Electric surface heating.
BS 6351-1: 1983 (1993)	Specification for electric surface heating devices.
BS 6351-2: 1983 (1993)	Guide to the design of electric surface heating systems.
BS 6351-3: 1983 (1993)	Code of practice for the installation, testing and maintenance of electric surface heating systems.
BS 6458	Fire hazard testing for electrotechnical products.
BS 6458-2.1: 1984	Glow-wire test.
BS 6651: 1999	Code of practice for protection of structures against lightning.
BS 6701: 1994	Code of practice for installation of apparatus intended for connection to certain telecommunications systems.
BS 6907	Electrical installations for open cast mines and quarries.
BS 7430: 1998	Code of practice for earthing.

BS 7454: 1991	Method for calculation of thermally permissible short-circuit currents taking into account non-adiabatic heating effects.
BS 7769	Electric cables, Calculation of current rating. Parts 1, 2, 3:1977.
BS 7697	Nominal voltages for low voltage public electricity supply systems.
BS 7822	Insulation coordination for equipment within low voltage systems.
BS 7822-1: 1995	Principles, requirements and tests.
BS EN 1648	Leisure accommodation vehicles. 12 V direct current extra low voltage electrical installations.
BS EN 1648-1: 1998	Caravans.
BS EN 1648-2: 1998	Motor caravans.
BS EN 50014: (1998)	Electrical apparatus for potentially explosive atmospheres. General requirements.
BS EN 50081	Electromagnetic compatibility Generic emission standard.
BS EN 50083	Electromagnetic compatibility Generic immunity standard. Partially replaced by BS EN 61000-6-2: 1999 but remains current.
BS EN 50265	Common test methods for cables under fire conditions. Test for resistance to vertical flame propagation for a single insulated conductor or cable.
BS EN 50265-1: 1999	Tests for resistance to vertical flame propagation for a single insulated conductor or cable. Apparatus.
BS EN 50265-2-1: 1999	Procedures. 1 kW pre-mixed flame.
BS EN 50265-2-2: 1999	Procedures. Diffusion flame.
BS EN 50281	Electrical apparatus for use in the presence of combustible dust.
BS EN 50310: 2000	Application of equipotential bonding and earthing in buildings with information technology equipment.
BS EN 60079	Electrical apparatus for potentially explosive gas atmospheres.
BS EN 60079-10: 1996	Classification of hazardous areas.

BS EN 60079-14: 1997	Electrical installations in hazardous areas (other than mines).
BS EN 60079-17: 1997	Inspection and maintenance of electrical installations in hazardous areas (other than mines).
BS EN 60445: 2000	Basic and safety principles for man-machine interface, marking and identification. Identification of equipment terminals and of terminations of certain designated conductors, including general rules for an alphanumeric system.
BS EN 60446: 2000	Basic and safety principles for the man-machine interface, marking and identification. Identification of conductors by colours or numerals.
BS EN 60617	Graphical symbols for diagrams. Replaces BS 3939.
BS EN 60950: 1992	Specification for safety of information technology equipment including electrical business equipment. Replaces BS 7002: 1989.

Appendix C

C

Section 1 Approved document B

- **Fire alarm and fire detection systems**
- **Protection of openings and fire stopping**

Extracts from Approved document B Fire Safety.

Please note that BS 5839 Part 1 has been revised in 2002 and BS 5839 Part 6 has been revised in 2004.

Fire alarm and fire detection systems

Introduction

1.1 Provisions are made in this section for suitable arrangements to be made in all buildings to give early warning in the event of fire. Paragraphs 1.2 to 1.22 deal with dwellings.

Dwellings

General

1.2 In most houses the installation of smoke alarms or automatic fire detection and alarm systems, can significantly increase the level of safety by automatically giving an early warning of fire.

1.3 If houses are not protected by an automatic fire detection and alarm system in accordance with the relevant recommendations of BS 5839: Part 1 Fire detection and alarm systems for buildings, Code of practice for system design, installation and servicing to at least an L3 standard, or BS 5839: Part 6 Code of practice for the design and installation of fire detection and alarm systems in dwellings to at least a Grade E type LD3 standard, they should be provided with a suitable number of smoke alarms installed in accordance with the guidance in paragraphs 1.4 to 1.22 below.

1.4 The smoke alarms should be mains-operated and conform to BS 5446 Components of automatic fire alarm systems for residential premises, Part 1 Specification for self-contained smoke alarms and point-type smoke detectors. They may have a secondary power supply such as a battery (either rechargeable or replaceable) or capacitor. More information on power supplies is given in clause 13 of BS 5839: Part 6: 1995.

Note: BS 5446: Part 1 covers smoke alarms based on ionization chamber smoke detectors and optical (photo-electric) smoke detectors. The different types of detector respond differently to smouldering and fast flaming fires. Either type of detector is generally suitable. However, the choice of detector type should, if possible, take into account the type of fire that might be expected and the need to avoid false alarms. Optical detectors tend to be less affected by low levels of 'invisible' smoke that often cause false alarms.

BS 5839: Part 6 suggests that, in general, optical smoke alarms should be installed in circulation spaces such as hallways and landings, and ionization chamber based smoke alarms may be the more appropriate type in rooms, such as the living room or dining room where a fast burning fire may present a greater danger to occupants than a smouldering fire.

Large houses

1.5 A house may be regarded as large if any of its storeys exceed 200 m^2.

1.6 A large house of more than 3 storeys (including basement storeys) should be fitted with an L2 system as described in BS 5839: Part 1: 1988, except that the provisions in clause 16.5 regarding duration of the standby supply need not be followed. However with unsupervised systems, the standby supply should be capable of automatically maintaining the system in normal operation (though with audible and visible indication of failure of the mains) for 72 hours, at the end of which sufficient capacity remains to supply the maximum alarm load for at least 15 minutes.

1.7 A large house of no more than 3 storeys (including basement storeys) may be fitted with an automatic fire detection and alarm system of Grade B type LD3 as described in BS 5839: Part 6 instead of an L2 system.

Loft conversions

1.8 Where a loft in a one or two storey house is converted into habitable accommodation, an automatic smoke detection and alarm system based on linked smoke alarms should be installed (see paragraph 2.26 of Approved document B).

Flats and maisonettes

1.9 The same principles apply within flats and maisonettes as for houses, while noting that:

a. the provisions are not intended to be applied to the common parts of blocks of flats and do not include interconnection between installations in separate flats;

b. a flat with accommodation on more than one level (ie a maisonette) should be treated in the same way as a house with more than one storey.

Note: Some student residential accommodation is constructed in the same way as a block of flats. Where groups of students share one flat with its own entrance door, it is appropriate to provide an automatic detection system within each flat. In student flats constructed on the compartmentation principles for flats in Section 9 (B3 of Approved document B), the automatic detection system will satisfy the requirements of Building Regulations if it gives a warning in the flat of fire origin. Where a general evacuation is required, the alarm system should follow the guidance in paragraph 1.30 of Approved document B.

Sheltered housing

1.10 The detection equipment in a sheltered housing scheme with a warden or supervisor, should have a connection to a central monitoring point (or central alarm relay station) so that the person in charge is aware that a fire has been detected in one of the dwellings, and can identify the dwelling concerned. These provisions are not intended to be applied to the common parts of a sheltered housing development, such as communal lounges, or to sheltered accommodation in the Institutional or Other residential purpose groups.

Installations based on smoke alarms

1.11 Smoke alarms should normally be positioned in the circulation spaces between sleeping spaces and places where fires are most likely to start (eg kitchens and living rooms) to pick up smoke in the early stages, while also being close enough to bedroom doors for the alarm to be effective when occupants are asleep.

1.12 In a house (including bungalows) there should be at least one smoke alarm on every storey.

1.13 Where more than one smoke alarm is installed they should be linked so that the detection of smoke by one unit operates the alarm signal in all of them. The manufacturers' instructions about the maximum number of units that can be linked should be observed.

1.14 Smoke alarms should be sited so that:

a. there is a smoke alarm in the circulation space within 7.5 m of the door to every habitable room;

b. where the kitchen area is not separated from the stairway or circulation space by a door, there should be a compatible interlinked heat detector in the kitchen, in addition to whatever smoke alarms are needed in the circulation space(s);

c. they are ceiling mounted and at least 300 mm from walls and light fittings (unless in the case of light fittings there is test evidence to prove that the proximity of the light fitting will not adversely affect the efficiency of the detector). Units designed for wall mounting may also be used provided that the units are above the level of doorways opening into the space, and they are fixed in accordance with manufacturers' instructions; and

d. the sensor in ceiling mounted devices is between 25 mm and 600 mm below the ceiling (25-150 mm in the case of heat detectors).

Note: This guidance applies to ceilings that are predominantly flat and horizontal.

1.15 It should be possible to reach the smoke alarms to carry out routine maintenance, such as testing and cleaning, easily and safely. For this reason smoke alarms should not be fixed over a stair shaft or any other opening between floors.

1.16 Smoke alarms should not be fixed next to or directly above heaters or air conditioning outlets. They should not be fixed in bathrooms, showers, cooking areas or garages, or any other place where steam, condensation or fumes could give false alarms. Smoke alarms should not be fitted in places that get very hot (such as a boiler room), or very cold (such as an unheated porch). They should not be fixed to surfaces which are normally much warmer or colder than the rest of the space, because the temperature difference might create air currents which move smoke away from the unit.

A requirement for maintenance cannot be made as a condition of passing plans by the Building Control Body. However the attention of developers and builders is drawn to the importance of providing the occupants with information on the use of the equipment, and on its maintenance (or guidance on suitable maintenance contractors).

Note: BS 5839: Part 1 and Part 6 recommend that occupiers should receive the manufacturers' instructions concerning the operation and maintenance of the alarm system.

Power supplies

1.17 The power supply for a smoke alarm system should be derived from the dwelling's mains electricity supply. The mains supply to the smoke alarm(s) should comprise a single independent circuit at the dwelling's main distribution board (consumer unit). If the smoke alarm installation does not include a standby power supply, no other electrical equipment should be connected to this circuit (apart from a dedicated monitoring device installed to indicate failure of the mains supply to the smoke alarms – see below).

1.18 A smoke alarm, or smoke alarm system, that includes a standby power supply or supplies, can operate during mains failure. It can therefore be connected to a regularly-used local lighting circuit. This has the advantage that the circuit is unlikely to be disconnected for any prolonged period.

1.19 Devices for monitoring the mains supply to the smoke alarm system may comprise audible or visible signals on each unit or on a dedicated mains monitor connected to the smoke alarm circuit. The circuit design of any mains failure monitor should avoid any significant reduction in the reliability of the supply, and should be sited so that the warning of failure is readily apparent to the occupants. If a continuous audible warning is given, it should be possible to silence it.

1.20 The smoke alarm circuit should preferably not be protected by any residual current device (RCD). However if electrical safety requires the use of an RCD, either:

a. the smoke alarm circuit should be protected by a single RCD which serves no other circuit; or

b. the RCD protection of a smoke alarm circuit should operate independently of any RCD protection for circuits supplying socket-outlets or portable equipment.

1.21 Any cable suitable for domestic wiring may be used for the power supply and interconnection to smoke alarm systems. It does not need any particular fire survival properties. Any conductors used for interconnecting alarms (signalling) should be readily distinguishable from those supplying mains power, eg by colour coding.

Note: Smoke alarms may be interconnected using radio-links, provided that this does not reduce the lifetime or duration of any standby power supply.

1.22 Other effective, though possibly more expensive, options exist. For example, the mains supply may be reduced to extra low voltage in a control unit incorporating a standby tricklecharged battery, before being distributed at that voltage to the alarms.

Fire alarm systems

1.25 All buildings should have arrangements for detecting fire. In most buildings fires are detected by people, either through observation or smell, and therefore often nothing more will be needed.

1.26 In small buildings/premises the means of raising the alarm may be simple. For instance, where all occupants are near to each other a shouted warning "FIRE" by the person discovering the fire may be all that is needed. In assessing the situation, it must be determined that the warning can be heard and understood throughout the premises, including for example the toilet areas. In other circumstances, manually operated sounders (such as rotary gongs or handbells) may be used. Alternatively a simple manual call point combined with a bell, battery and charger may be suitable.

In all other cases, the building should be provided with a suitable electrically operated fire warning system with manual call points sited adjacent to exit doors and sufficient sounders to be clearly audible throughout the building.

1.27 An electrically operated fire alarm system should comply with BS 5839: Part 1 Fire detection and alarm systems for buildings, Code of practice for system design, installation and servicing.

Call points for electrical alarm systems should comply with BS 5839: Part 2 Specification for manual call points, or Type A of BS EN 54 Fire detection and fire alarm systems – Part 11: Manual call points, and these should be installed in accordance with BS 5839: Part 1. Type B call points should only be used with the approval of the Building Control Body.

Note 1: BS 5839: Part 1 specifies four types of system, ie type L for the protection of life; type M manual alarm systems; type P for property protection; and type X for multi-occupancy buildings. Type L systems are subdivided into L1 – systems installed throughout the protected building; L2 – systems installed only in defined parts of the protected building (a type L2 system should normally include the coverage required of a type L3 system) and L3 – systems installed only for the protection of escape routes. Type P systems are subdivided into P1 – systems installed throughout the protected building and P2 – systems installed only in defined parts of the protected building.

Note 2: BS EN 54-11 covers two types of call points, Type A (direct operation) in which the change to the alarm condition is automatic (i.e. without the need for further manual action) when the frangible element is broken or displaced; and Type B (indirect operation) in which the change to the alarm condition requires a separate manual operation of the operating element by the user after the frangible element is broken or displaced.

1.28 If it is considered that people might not respond quickly to a fire warning, or where people are unfamiliar with the fire warning arrangements, consideration may be given to installing a voice alarm system. Such a system could form part of a public address system and give both an audible signal and verbal instructions in the event of fire.

The fire warning signal should be distinct from other signals which may be in general use and be accompanied by clear verbal instructions.

If a voice alarm system is to be installed, it should comply with BS 5839: Part 8 Code of practice for the design, installation and servicing of voice alarm systems.

1.29 In certain premises, eg large shops and places of assembly, an initial general alarm may be undesirable because of the number of members of the public present. The need for fully trained staff to effect pre-planned procedures for safe evacuation will therefore be essential. Actuation of the fire alarm system will cause staff to be alerted, eg by discreet sounders, personal paging systems etc. Provision will normally be made for full evacuation of the premises by sounders or a message broadcast over the public address system. In all other respects, any staff alarm system should comply with BS 5839: Part 1.

Automatic fire detection and fire alarm systems

1.30 Automatic fire detection and alarms in accordance with BS 5839: Part 1 should be provided in Institutional and Other residential occupancies.

1.31 Automatic fire detection systems are not normally needed in Office, Shop and commercial, Assembly and recreation, Industrial, and Storage and other non-residential occupancies. However, there are often circumstances where a fire detection system in accordance with BS 5839: Part 1 may be needed. For example:

a. to compensate for some departure from the guidance elsewhere in this document;

b. as part of the operating system for some fire protection systems, such as pressure differential systems or automatic door releases;

c. where a fire could break out in an unoccupied part of the premises (eg a storage area or basement that is not visited on a regular basis, or a part of the building that has been temporarily vacated) and prejudice the means of escape from any occupied part(s) of the premises.

Notes:
1. General guidance on the standard of automatic fire detection that may need to be provided within a building can be found in the Home Office guides that support the Fire Precautions Act 1971 and the Fire Precautions (Workplace) Regulations 1997 and, in the case of the Institutional purpose group, in "Firecode".

2. Guidance on the provision of automatic fire detection within a building which is designed for phased evacuation can be found in paragraph 5.20 of Approved document B.

3. Where an atrium building is designed in accordance BS 5588: Fire precautions in the design, construction and use of buildings, Part 7 Code of practice for the incorporation of atria in buildings, then the relevant recommendations in that code for the installation of fire alarm/fire detection systems for the design option(s) selected should be followed.

Design and installation of systems

1.32 It is essential that fire detection and fire warning systems are properly designed, installed and maintained. Where a fire alarm system is installed, an installation and commissioning certificate should be provided. Third party certification schemes for fire protection products and related services are an effective means of providing the fullest possible assurances, offering a level of quality, reliability and safety (see paragraph 0.20 of Approved document B).

Houses

9.13 Every wall separating semi-detached houses, or houses in terraces, should be constructed as a compartment wall, and the houses should be considered as separate buildings.

9.14 If a domestic garage is attached to (or forms an integral part of) a house, the garage should be separated from the rest of the house, as shown in Diagram 25.

Note: The walls and floors shown in Diagram 25 are not compartment walls and compartment floors, and the 100 mm difference in level between the garage floor and the door opening is to prevent any leakage of petrol vapour into the dwelling.

See para 9.14

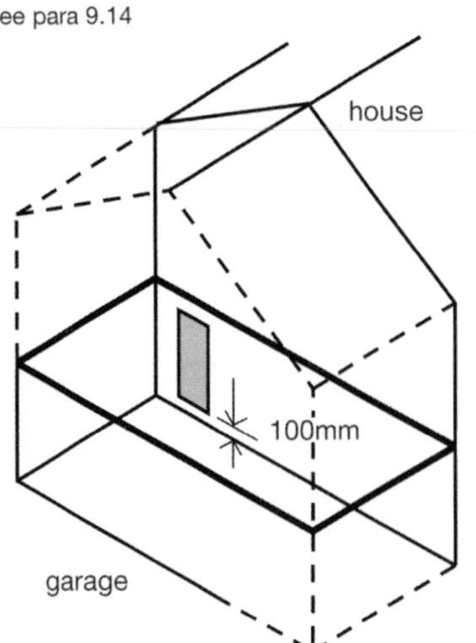

Diagram 25 Separation between garage and dwelling house

Flats

9.15 In buildings containing flats or maisonettes the following should be constructed as compartment walls or compartment floors:

a. every floor (unless it is within a maisonette, ie between one storey and another within one dwelling); and

b. every wall separating a flat or maisonette from any other part of the building; and

Note: "any other part of the building" does not include an external balcony/deck access.

c. every wall enclosing a refuse storage chamber.

Other residential buildings

9.19 All floors should be constructed as compartment floors.

Protection of openings and fire stopping

Introduction

11.1 Sections 9 and 10 of Approved document B make provisions for fire separating elements, and set out the circumstances in which there may be openings in them. This Section deals with the protection of openings in such elements.

11.2 If a fire separating element is to be effective, then every joint, or imperfection of fit, or opening to allow services to pass through the element, should be adequately protected by sealing or firestopping so that the fire resistance of the element is not impaired.

11.3 The measures in this section are intended to delay the passage of fire. They generally have the additional benefit of retarding smoke spread, but the test specified in Appendix A of Approved document B for integrity does not stipulate criteria for the passage of smoke as such.

11.4 Detailed guidance on door openings and fire doors is given in Appendix B of Approved document B.

Table 15 Maximum nominal internal diameter of pipes passing through a compartment wall/floor (see para 11.5 et seq)

Situation	Pipe material and maximum nominal internal diameter (mm)		
	(a) Non-combustible material [1]	(b) Lead, aluminium aluminium alloy uPVC [2], fibre cement	(c) Any other material
1. Structure (but not a wall separating buildings) enclosing a protected shaft which is not a stairway or a lift shaft	160	110	40
2. Wall separating dwelling houses, or compartment wall or compartment floor between flats	160	160 (stack pipe)[3] 110 (branch pipe)[3]	40
3. Any other situation	160	40	40

Notes:

1. Any non-combustible material (such as cast iron, copper or steel) which if exposed to a temperature of 800°C, will not soften or fracture to the extent that flame or hot gas will pass through the wall of the pipe.
2. uPVC pipes complying with BS 4514 and uPVC pipes complying with BS 5255.
3. These diameters are only in relation to pipes forming part of an above-ground drainage system and enclosed as shown in Diagram 38. In other cases the maximum diameters against situation 3 apply.

Openings for pipes

11.5 Pipes which pass through a compartment wall or compartment floor (unless the pipe is in a protected shaft), or through a cavity barrier, should meet the appropriate provisions in alternatives A, B or C below.

Alternative A: Proprietary seals (any pipe diameter)

11.6 Provide a proprietary sealing system which has been shown by test to maintain the fire resistance of the wall, floor or cavity barrier.

Alternative B: Pipes with a restricted diameter

11.7 Where a proprietary sealing system is not used, fire-stopping may be used around the pipe, keeping the opening as small as possible. The nominal internal diameter of the pipe should not be more than the relevant dimension given in Table 15.

11.8 The diameters given in Table 15 for pipes of specification (b) used in situation (2) assume that the pipes are part of an above-ground drainage system and are enclosed as shown in Diagram 38 of Approved document B. If they are not, the smaller diameter given in situation (3) should be used.

Alternative C: Sleeving

11.9 A pipe of lead, aluminium, aluminium alloy, fibre-cement or uPVC, with a maximum nominal internal diameter of 160 mm, may be used with a sleeving of non-combustible pipe as shown in Diagram 37. The specification for non-combustible and uPVC pipes is given in the notes to Table 15.

See para 11.9, alternative method C

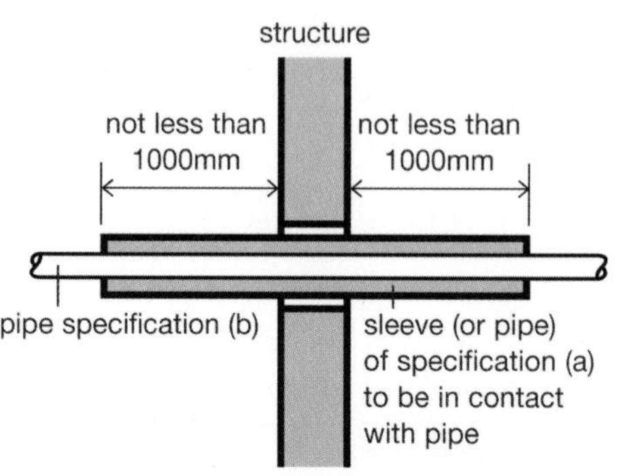

Diagram 37 Pipes penetrating structure

Notes:

1 Make the opening in the structure as small as possible and provide fire-stopping between pipe and structure.
2 See Table 15 for materials specification.

Appendix D
EAS framework for minimum technical competences of enterprises

Appendix D Minimum Technical Competence of Enterprises that undertake Electrical Installation Work in Dwellings

The document "Minimum Technical Competence of Enterprises that undertake Electrical Installation Work in Dwellings" reproduced here has been prepared by the Board of the Electrotechnical Assessment Scheme (EAS) at the request of the Office of the Deputy Prime Minister to be used as a measure of the technical competency to be required by competent scheme operators of enterprises seeking registration.

The information included in this Appendix is correct at the time of going to press; however, it is currently under review and may change. Refer to the IEE website www.iee.org/technical

Minimum Technical Competence of Enterprises that undertake Electrical Installation Work in Dwellings (6 October 2004 draft).

1 Scope

This document sets out the minimum requirements for an enterprise to undertake electrical installation work in dwellings safely.

The document defines the requirements in relation to three levels of activity for enterprises:

Level A The requirements for an enterprise the scope of whose work includes the design, installation, inspection and testing of all electrical installation work that is associated with dwellings and is intended to operate at low or extra-low voltage.

Level B The requirements for an enterprise the scope of whose work is limited to the design, installation, inspection and testing of defined electrical installation work, intended to operate at low or extra-low voltage, that is associated with dwellings and is undertaken in connection with, or ancillary to, some other work. (See Annex 7 for an indicative list of non-electrical work in connection with which electrical work in dwellings is carried out.)

Level C The requirements for an enterprise, the scope of whose electrical installation work is limited to minor electrical installation work, intended to operate at low or extra-low voltage, that is associated with dwellings and is undertaken in connection with, or ancillary to, some other work. (See Annex 7 for indicative list of work in connection with which electrical work in dwellings is carried out.)

2. Definitions

Assessed Enterprise – an enterprise which has been assessed in accordance with the requirements of this document as competent, and which possesses a current Assessment Certificate.

BS 7671– Current edition including all amendments.

Building Regulations – In England and Wales, the Building Act 1984 (as amended) and all subsequent Building Regulations (Amendment) Regulations.

Competence – in possession of the necessary technical knowledge, skill and experience for the nature of the electrical work undertaken and able to prevent danger or where appropriate injury.

Directly engaged – carrying out electrical installation work in dwellings, including the design, installation, inspection, testing and certification of that work in accordance with the requirements of BS 7671.

Dwelling – includes a dwelling house or flat.

Electrical installation work – the design, installation, inspection and testing of electrical equipment as a system or part of a system.

Electrical installation work in dwellings – work on electrical installations, carried out by, and under the direct control and supervision of an Enterprise, intended to operate at low voltage or extra-low voltage, in dwellings, in common parts of buildings serving one or more dwellings other than power supplies to lifts, buildings which receive their electricity from a source located within or shared with a dwelling, or in gardens or in or on land associated with buildings where the electricity is from sources located within or shared with dwellings. It excludes reporting on the condition of existing electrical installations.

Enterprise – each address and trading title of a sole trader, partnership, private limited company, public limited company, public body or other legal entity.

Flat – a separate and self contained premises constructed or adapted for use for residential purposes and forming part of a building from some other part from which it is divided horizontally.

Functionality – the ability of a completed installation to operate as required.

Minor Electrical Installation Works – additions, alterations and replacements to domestic electrical installations that do not extend to the provision of a new circuit or a new protective device.

Principal – head of the enterprise, eg. sole trader, partner of a partnership, managing director, etc.

Principal Duty Holder – the person appointed by the enterprise to have responsibility for the maintenance of the overall standard and safety of the electrical installation work in dwellings.

Qualified Supervisor – a competent person with specific responsibility on a day-to-day basis for the safety, technical standard and quality of electrical installation work in dwellings.

Sub-letting – engaging another enterprise or individual to carry out domestic electrical installation work (Note: employing staff on a labour-only basis is not sub-letting).

Level A: REQUIREMENTS RELATING TO THE COMPETENCE OF AN ENTERPRISE TO DESIGN, INSTALL, INSPECT AND TEST ALL FIXED ELECTRICAL INSTALLATIONS IN DWELLINGS

A1. Electrical Installation Work

A1.1 The enterprise shall be directly engaged in carrying out electrical installation work in dwellings.

A1.2 The electrical installation work in dwellings shall be carried out in compliance with the relevant technical reference documents (see Annex 2).

A1.3 An assessed enterprise shall not sub-let electrical installation work in dwellings unless the work is undertaken by an enterprise which is registered with one of the Part P self-certification schemes listed by Government in Schedule 2A of SI 2004/1808.

A1.4 Competence of the enterprise will not be assessed on electrical installation work sub-let to others; however the assessed enterprise will retain responsibility for this work.

A2. Technical reference documents

A2.1 The enterprise shall have current editions, including all amendments, of the documents listed in Annex 2.

A3. Test instruments

A3.1 The enterprise shall have an adequate number of serviceable test instruments and test leads appropriate to the range, scale and geographical spread of electrical installation work in dwellings carried out. As a minimum the enterprise shall have instruments and leads to enable the tests detailed in Annex 3 to be carried out.

A3.2 The enterprise shall have a suitable system in place to ensure that all test instruments used for the certification of electrical installation work in dwellings, whether owned or hired by the enterprise, are accurate and consistent (see Annex 1).

A3.3 The assessed enterprise shall hold records demonstrating the accuracy and consistency of test instruments used for certification of electrical installation work in dwellings for a minimum of three years.

A4. Certification and reporting

A4.1 The enterprise shall issue the appropriate electrical installation certificates in accordance with the relevant standards (see Annex 2) for all the electrical installation work in dwellings that it carries out.

A4.2 The assessed enterprise shall issue the appropriate Building Regulations compliance certificates in accordance with the relevant standards and regulations (see Annex 2) for all the electrical installation work in dwellings that it carries out.

A4.3 The assessed enterprise shall hold copies of all the certificates that it has issued for electrical installation work in dwellings for at least three years.

A5. Personnel

A5.1 The enterprise shall employ persons to carry out electrical installation work in dwellings who are competent and/or adequately supervised to ensure safety during and on completion of the work.

A5.2 The enterprise shall appoint an individual to be the Principal Duty Holder. In addition, the enterprise shall appoint as Qualified Supervisors as many individuals as necessary to ensure all electrical installation work in dwellings is under the control of a Qualified Supervisor. The Principal Duty Holder may also be a Qualified Supervisor.

A5.3 The Principal Duty Holders hold responsibilities detailed in A5.5.

A5.4 Qualified Supervisors hold responsibilities as detailed in A5.6 and must meet the requirements set out in A5.7.

A5.5 Responsibilities of the Principal Duty Holder

A5.5.1 To ensure that the enterprise carries out all electrical installation work in dwellings in accordance with the relevant standards, including the issue of certification, and;

A5.5.2 to ensure that the enterprise carries out all electrical installation work in dwellings in compliance with all relevant statutory requirements, including the issue of certification, and;

A5.5.3 have an understanding of, and be responsible for the health and safety and other statutory requirements relating to electrical installation work in dwellings carried out by the enterprise, and;

A5.5.4 to ensure that all electrical installation work in dwellings is allocated to the enterprise's Qualified Supervisor(s).

A5.6 Responsibilities of a Qualified Supervisor

A5.6.1 The safety, quality and technical standard on a day-to-day basis of the electrical installation work in dwellings is allocated to him/her.

A5.7 Requirements for a Qualified Supervisor

A Qualified Supervisor shall:

A5.7.1 ensure that the results of the inspection and testing are accurately recorded on the appropriate forms of certification, and;

A5.7.2 verify and authenticate certification showing compliance with Building Regulations

A5.7.3 have adequate knowledge, experience and understanding of the design, installation, inspection and testing procedures for electrical installation work in dwellings as specified in Annex 4, and;

A5.7.4 meet the competence requirements set out in Annex 5, and;

A5.7.5 satisfy the minimum requirements for training and experience set out in Annex 6.

A6. Insurance

A6.1 The enterprise shall hold at least £2 million of public liability insurance covering all the electrical installation work it carries out in dwellings.

A7. Complaints

A7.1 The assessed enterprise shall maintain a record of all complaints received over at least the previous three years, concerning the compliance with Building Regulations of the electrical installation work it has carried out in dwellings, together with the details of the actions taken to resolve these complaints.

A8. Health and Safety

A8.1 The enterprise shall have a written health and safety policy statement where required by law, and will carry out risk assessments as appropriate.

A9. Records

In addition to those records detailed previously, the assessed enterprise shall also hold for at least three years:

A9.1 Specifications, drawings and certificates relating to electrical installation work in dwellings, carried out and in progress.

A9.2 A list of all electrical installation work carried out in dwellings.

Level B: REQUIREMENTS RELATING TO THE COMPETENCE OF AN ENTERPRISE TO UNDERTAKE DEFINED ELECTRICAL INSTALLATION WORK IN DWELLINGS IN CONNECTION WITH, OR ANCILLARY TO, SOME OTHER NON-ELECTRICAL WORK

B1. Defined Electrical Installation Work

B1.1 The enterprise shall be directly engaged in carrying out defined electrical installation work in dwellings.

B1.2 The electrical installation work in dwellings shall be carried out in compliance with the relevant technical reference documents (see Annex 2).

B1.3 An assessed enterprise shall not sub-let electrical installation work in dwellings unless the work is undertaken by an enterprise which is appropriately registered with one of the Part P self-certification schemes listed by Government in Schedule 2A of SI 2004/1808.

B1.4 Competence of the enterprise will not be assessed on electrical installation work sub-let to others; however, the assessed enterprise will retain responsibility for this work.

B1.5 Defined electrical installation work is electrical work that is provided solely within the scope of electrical installation work defined for the enterprise.

B2. Technical reference documents

B2.1 The enterprise shall have current editions, including all amendments, of the documents listed in Annex 2.

B3. Test instruments

B3.1 The enterprise shall have an adequate number of serviceable test instruments and test leads appropriate to the range, scale and geographical spread of electrical installation work in dwellings carried out. As a minimum the enterprise shall have instruments and leads to enable the tests detailed in Annex 3 to be carried out.

B.3.2 The enterprise shall have a suitable system in place to ensure that all test instruments used for the certification of electrical installation work in dwellings, whether owned or hired by the enterprise, are accurate and consistent (see Annex 1).

B.3.3 The assessed enterprise shall hold records demonstrating the accuracy and consistency of test instruments used for certification of electrical installation work in dwellings for a minimum of three years.

B4. Certification and reporting

B4.1 The enterprise shall issue the appropriate electrical installation certificates in accordance with the relevant standards and regulations (see Annex 2) for all the electrical installation work in dwellings that it carries out.

B4.2 The assessed enterprise shall issue the appropriate Building Regulations compliance certificates in accordance with the relevant standards and regulations (see Annex 2) for all the electrical installation work in dwellings that it carries out.

B4.3 The assessed enterprise shall hold copies of all the certificates that it has issued for electrical installation work in dwellings for at least three years.

B5. Personnel

B5.1 The enterprise shall appoint an individual to be the Principal Duty Holder.

B5.2 The Principal Duty Holder holds responsibilities detailed in B5.4.

B5.3 All electrical installation work in dwellings shall be carried out by an individual holding current and appropriate competence as detailed in B5.5.

B5.4 Responsibilities of the Principal Duty Holder:

B5.4.1 To ensure that the enterprise carries out all electrical installation work in dwellings in accordance with the relevant standards, including the issue of certification, and;

B5.4.2 to ensure that the enterprise carries out all electrical installation work in dwellings in compliance with all relevant statutory requirements, including the issue of certification, and;

B5.4.3 have an understanding of, and be responsible for the health and safety and other statutory requirements relating to electrical installation work in dwellings carried out by the enterprise, and;

B5.4.4 to ensure that all electrical installation work in dwellings is allocated to an individual with the current, appropriate competence as detailed in B5.6, and;

B5.4.5 to ensure that electrical installation work in dwellings that goes beyond the enterprise's defined scope of electrical installation work, as described at the start of this document, is referred back to the customer for execution by an enterprise that has the necessary scope.

B5.5 Individual's responsibilities

B5.5.1 The safety, quality and technical standard of the electrical installation work in dwellings allocated to him/her on a day-to-day basis.

B5.6 Individual's requirements and competence

Individuals who carry out electrical installation work in dwellings shall:

B5.6.1 ensure that the results of the inspection and testing are accurately recorded on the appropriate forms of certification, and;

B5.6.2 verify and authenticate certification showing compliance with Building Regulations, and;

B5.6.3 have adequate knowledge, experience and understanding of the design, installation, inspection, testing, verification and certification procedures for electrical installation work in dwellings as set out in Annex 4, and;

B5.6.4 meet the competence requirements set out in Annex 5, appropriate to the work being carried out, and;

B5.6.5 satisfy the minimum appropriate requirements for training and experience set out in Annex 6.

B6. Insurance

B6.1 The enterprise shall hold at least £2 million of public liability insurance covering all the electrical installation work it carries out in dwellings.

B7. Complaints

B7.1 The enterprise shall maintain a record of all complaints received over at least the previous three years, concerning the compliance with Building Regulations of the electrical installation work it has carried out in dwellings, together with the details of the actions taken to resolve these complaints.

B8. Health and Safety

B8.1 The enterprise shall have a written health and safety policy statement where required by law and will carry out risk assessments as appropriate.

B9. Records

In addition to those records detailed previously, the assessed enterprise shall also hold for at least three years:

B9.1 Specifications, drawings and certificates relating to electrical installation work in dwellings, carried out and in progress.

B9.2 A list of all electrical installation work carried out in dwellings.

Level C: REQUIREMENTS RELATING TO THE COMPETENCE OF AN ENTERPRISE TO UNDERTAKE MINOR ELECTRICAL INSTALLATION WORK IN DWELLINGS IN CONNECTION WITH, OR ANCILLARY TO, SOME OTHER NON-ELECTRICAL WORK

C1. Minor electrical installation work

C1.1 The enterprise shall be directly engaged in carrying out minor electrical installation work in dwellings.

C1.2 The electrical installation work in dwellings shall be carried out in compliance with the relevant technical reference documents (see Annex 2).

C1.3 An assessed enterprise shall not sub-let electrical installation work in dwellings unless the work is undertaken by an enterprise which is appropriately registered with one of the Part P self-certification schemes listed by Government in Schedule 2A of SI 2004/1808.

C1.4 Competence of the enterprise will not be assessed on electrical installation work sub-let to others; however, the assessed enterprise will retain responsibility for this work.

C1.5 Minor electrical installation work is electrical work involving additions, alterations and replacements to domestic electrical installations that do not extend to the provision of a new circuit or a new protective device.

C2. Technical Reference Documents

C2.1 The enterprise shall have current editions, including all amendments, of the documents listed in Annex 2.

C3. Test instruments

C3.1 The enterprise shall have an adequate number of serviceable test instruments and test leads appropriate to the range, scale and geographical spread of electrical installation work in dwellings carried out. As a minimum the enterprise shall have instruments and leads to enable the tests detailed in Annex 3 to be carried out.

C.3.2 The enterprise shall have a suitable system in place to ensure that all test instruments used for the certification of electrical installation work in dwellings, whether owned or hired by the enterprise, are accurate and consistent (see Annex 1).

C.3.3 The assessed enterprise shall hold records demonstrating the accuracy and consistency of test instruments used for certification of electrical installation work in dwellings for a minimum of three years.

C4 Certification and reporting

C4.1 The enterprise shall issue the appropriate electrical installation certificates in accordance with the relevant standards and regulations (see Annex 2) for all the electrical installation work in dwellings that it carries out.

C4.2 The assessed enterprise shall issue the appropriate Building Regulations compliance certificates in accordance with the relevant standards and regulations (see Annex 2) for all the electrical installation work in dwellings that it carries out.

C4.3 The assessed enterprise shall hold copies of all the certificates that it has issued for electrical installation work in dwellings for at least three years.

C5. Personnel

C5.1 The enterprise shall appoint an individual to be the Principal Duty Holder.

C5.2 The Principal Duty Holder holds responsibilities detailed in C5.4.

C5.3 All electrical installation work in dwellings shall be carried out by an individual holding current and appropriate competence as detailed in C5.5.

C5.4 Responsibilities of the Principal Duty Holder

C5.4.1 To ensure that the enterprise carries out all electrical installation work in dwellings in accordance with the relevant standards, including the issue of certification, and;

C5.4.2 to ensure that the enterprise carries out all electrical installation work in dwellings in compliance with all relevant statutory requirements, including the issue of certification, and;

C5.4.3 have an understanding of, and be responsible for the health and safety and other statutory requirements relating to electrical installation work in dwellings carried out by the enterprise, and;

C5.4.4 to ensure that all electrical installation work in dwellings is allocated to an individual with the current, appropriate competence as detailed in C5.6, and;

C5.4.5 to ensure that electrical installation work in dwellings that goes beyond minor electrical installation work, as defined, is referred back to the customer for execution by an enterprise that has the necessary scope.

C5.5 Individual's responsibilities

C5.5.1 The safety, quality and technical standard of the electrical installation work in dwellings allocated to him/her on a day-to-day basis.

C5.6 Individual's requirements and competence

Individuals who carry out electrical installation work in dwellings shall:

C5.6.1 ensure that the results of the inspection and testing are accurately recorded on the appropriate forms of certification, and;

C5.6.2 verify and authenticate certification showing compliance with Building Regulations, and;

C5.6.3 have adequate knowledge, experience and understanding of the design, installation, inspection, testing, verification and certification procedures for electrical installation work in dwellings as set out in Annex 4, and;

C5.6.4 meet the competence requirements set out in Annex 5, appropriate to the work being carried out, and;

C5.6.5 satisfy the minimum appropriate requirements for training and experience set out in Annex 6.

C6. Insurance

C6.1 The enterprise shall hold at least £2 million of public liability insurance covering all the electrical installation work it carries out in dwellings.

C7. Complaints

C7.1 The enterprise shall maintain a record of all complaints received over at least the previous three years, concerning the compliance with Building Regulations of the electrical installation work it has carried out in dwellings, together with the details of the actions taken to resolve these complaints.

C8. Health and Safety

C8.1 The enterprise shall have a written health and safety policy statement where required by law and will carry out risk assessments as appropriate.

C9. Records

In addition to those records detailed previously, the assessed enterprise shall also hold for at least three years:

C9.1 Specifications, drawings and certificates relating to electrical installation work in dwellings, carried out and in progress.

C9.2 A list of all electrical installation work carried out in dwellings.

Annex 1

TEST INSTRUMENTS – CALIBRATION REQUIREMENTS

The Enterprise shall have a suitable system in place to ensure that the accuracy and consistency of all test instruments used for certification and reporting purposes is being maintained.

There are a number of alternatives for such control systems, including:

- Maintaining records of the formal calibration/re-calibration of test instruments as recommended by the instrument manufacturers, supported by calibration certificates issued by recognised organisations with measurements traceable to national standards. Certificates issued by UKAS accredited laboratories are preferable.

- Maintaining records over time of comparative cross-checks with other test instruments used by the Electrical Contractor.

- Maintaining records over time of measurements of the characteristics of designated reference circuits or devices. For example, the consistency of continuity, insulation resistance and earth electrode test instruments could be checked against a proprietary resistance box or a set of suitable resistors. Earth fault loop impedance test instruments could be checked by carrying out tests on a designated socket-outlet (on a non-RCD protected circuit) in the contractor's office. RCD test instruments could be checked by carrying out tests on an RCD unit plugged into the designated socket-outlet.

Annex 2

TECHNICAL REFERENCE DOCUMENTS

Minimum requirement relative to assessed level of enterprise

Technical Reference Document	Level A	Level B	Level C
BS 7671: Requirements for Electrical Installations	Yes	Not essential	Not essential
IEE On-Site Guide to BS 7671: 16th Edition Wiring Regulations or equivalent	Not essential	Yes	Yes
HS(R)25 Memorandum of Guidance on the Electricity at Work Regulations	Yes	Yes	Yes
Building Regulations, Approved document P	Yes	Yes	Yes

Annex 3

TEST INSTRUMENTS

Minimum requirement relative to assessed level of the enterprise – test instruments and suitable leads to enable the following tests to be carried out:

Test Instrument	Level A	Level B	Level C
Voltage indication	Yes	Yes	Yes
Insulation resistance testing	Yes	Yes	Yes
Continuity testing	Yes	Yes	Yes
Phase/earth loop impedance for testing of power and lighting circuits	Yes	Yes	Yes
External earth loop impedance	Yes	Yes	Not essential
Residual current device testing	Yes	Yes	Yes

Annex 4

KNOWLEDGE AND SKILL REQUIREMENTS RELATIVE TO ASSESSED LEVEL OF THE ENTERPRISE

Qualified Supervisor Level A	Individual Operative Defined electrical installation work Level B	Individual Operative Minor works Level C
Appropriate qualifications knowledge, understanding and experience of the design, installation, inspection and testing procedures for all electrical installation work in dwellings in accordance with BS 7671	Appropriate qualifications knowledge, understanding and experience of the design, installation, inspection and testing procedures for defined electrical installation work in dwellings in accordance with BS 7671	Appropriate qualifications knowledge, understanding and experience of the design, installation inspection and testing procedures for minor electrical installation work in dwellings in accordance with BS 7671
Carry out appropriate inspection and testing as detailed in BS 7671	Carry out appropriate inspection and testing as detailed in BS 7671	Carry out appropriate inspection and testing as detailed in BS 7671
Health and Safety – safe working and reinstatement of circuits	Health and Safety – safe working and reinstatement of circuits	Health and Safety – safe working and reinstatement of circuits
Building Regulations relevant to electrical installation work in dwellings	Building Regulations relevant to electrical installation work in dwellings	Building Regulations relevant to electrical installation work in dwellings

Annex 5

TECHNICAL COMPETENCE REQUIREMENTS RELATIVE TO ASSESSED LEVEL OF THE ENTERPRISE

No	Technical Competence	Level A Qualified Supervisor	Level B Individual Operative	Level C Individual Operative
1.	Applicable Building Regulations	Yes	Yes	Yes
2.	Electrical Safety legislation, regulations standards and terminology:			
	2.1 Fundamental Principles	Yes	Yes	Yes
	2.2 Construction Design and Management	Yes	Where relevant	Where relevant
	2.3 Electrical Safety in Construction	Yes	Where relevant	Where relevant
3.	Pre-work survey/inspection:			
	3.1 Rationale for alterations to circuits & Adequacy for load increase	Yes	Yes	Yes
	3.2 Three-phase requirements	Yes	Where necessary	Not necessary
	3.3 Additional criteria for New Works	Yes	Yes	Not necessary
4.	Safe isolation procedures	Yes	Yes	Yes
5.	Identification of unsafe electrical situations – including documented procedures following unsafe situation	Yes	Yes	Yes
6.	Earthing and bonding requirements – including earthing system types	Yes	Yes	Yes
7.	Electrical test procedures – including external earth fault loop impedance	Yes	Yes	Not necessary
8.	Cable and component selection			
	8.1 compliance with standards & Conventional final circuits cables	Yes	Yes	Yes
	8.2 new circuits	Yes	Yes	Not necessary
9.	Installation and replacement of electrical components	Yes	Yes	Yes
10.	Checking the correct and safe operation of installed electrical components – including Inspection Check List	Yes	Yes	Yes

continued

No	Technical Competence	Level A Qualified Supervisor	Level B Individual Operative	Level C Individual Operative
11.	Recording of electrical test results and completion of certification	Yes	Yes	Yes
	11.1 Certification for new circuits	Yes	Yes	Not necessary
12.	Installing and/or rerouting cables	Yes	Yes	Not necessary
	12.1 External cabling & Safe Zones	Yes	Where relevant	Not necessary
13.	Special Locations:			
	13.1 Locations containing a bath or a shower	Yes	Where relevant	Where relevant
	13.2 Shower cubicles in a room used for other purposes	Yes	Where relevant	Where relevant
	13.3 Garden Buildings, Domestic Garages and External Equipment	Yes	Where relevant	Where relevant
	13.4 Earthing requirements of equipment having high protective conductor current	Yes	Where relevant	Not necessary
14.	New circuit requirements	Yes	Where relevant	Not permitted
15.	Lighting installations	Yes	Where relevant	Where relevant
16.	Maintenance	Yes	Where relevant	Where relevant
17.	3-phase supplies	Yes	Where relevant	Not necessary

Level B: The electrical work covered by this level will be only in connection with, or ancillary to, some other non-electrical work carried out within domestic premises and will be limited to work within the scope defined for the enterprise.

Level C: The electrical work covered by this level will be only in connection with, or ancillary to, some other non-electrical work. Work carried out within domestic premises will be limited to a single-phase supply at nominal voltages not exceeding 230 V a.c. and confined to alterations to or an extension of an existing circuit. (See Annex 7 for indicative list of non-electrical work.)

Reference Documents: The assessment of competence is based on the following documents:

- HSE Memorandum of guidance on The Electricity at Work Regulations (HSR 25);
- Building Regulations Approved document P;
- British Standard 7671: 2001;
- IEE On-Site Guide to BS 7671: 2001;
- Cable, component and fitting manufacturers Installation and Testing Instructions where relevant;
- IEE Guidance Notes 1 – 7.

Annex 6

QUALIFICATION REQUIREMENTS

The Qualified Supervisor (Level A) or Individual Operative (Level B or C) shall have one of the following qualifications, or an equivalent qualification:

City & Guilds 2381

Domestic Electrical Installer Qualification – (National Accredited Qualification)

City & Guilds 2380 (16th Edition) Certificate

City & Guilds 2360 Part 2 (Electrical Installation Competencies), passed in 1993 or after

NVQ/SVQ level 3 in installing and commissioning electrotechnical systems and equipment awarded in 1993 or after

The Scottish Qualification Authority Tailored Award in Design and Verification of Electrical Installation

City and Guilds 2400.

Annex 7

EXAMPLES OF WORK in connection with which electrical work in dwellings is carried out

- Plumbing
- Gas installation work
- Installation of oil-fired combustion appliances
- Installation of solid fuel burning combustion appliances
- Installation or refurbishment of kitchens, bathrooms or bedrooms
- Stair-lift installation work
- Loft conversions
- Air conditioning installation work
- Building extensions
- Building conservatories
- Installation of domestic extractor fans
- Installation of security systems
- Installation of telecommunications systems
- Installation of door or gate entry systems
- CCTV systems
- Property maintenance
- Spa bath installations
- Swimming pool installations.

Appendix E
Electrical self-certification schemes

- Part A Full Competence Schemes
- Part B Defined Competence Schemes
- Management of a Defined Competence Scheme
- Minimum standard of technical competence for Part P schemes

Competent persons self-certification schemes under the Building Regulations for Electrical Safety in Dwellings

Note this list was current at the time of going to press, but enquirers should obtain an up-to-date list from the IEE website:

http://www.iee.org/Publish/WireRegs/index.cfm

Part A Full Competence Schemes

For an enterprise the scope of whose work includes the design, installation, inspection and testing of all electrical installation work that is associated with dwellings and is intended to operate at low or extra-low voltage.

(1) BRE Certification Ltd
Bucknalls Lane,
Garston, Watford WD25 9XX
Tel: 0870 609 6093
Fax: 01923 664603
Email enquiries@brecertification.co.uk
Web: www.partp.co.uk

(2) British Standards Institution
BSI Product Services
Maylands Avenue,
Hemel Hempstead HP2 4SQ.
Tel: 01442 230442
Web: www.bsi-global.com/Kitemark/ElectricalInstallers

(3) ELECSA Ltd.
44 – 48 Borough High Street,
London SE1 1XB
Tel: +44 (0) 870 749 0080
Fax: +44 (0) 870 749 0085
Email: enquiries@elecsa.org.uk
Web: www.elecsa.org.uk

(4) Napit Certification Services Ltd
The Gardners Lodge
Pleasely Vale Business Park, Mansfield,
Nottinghamshire NG19 8RL
Tel: 0870 444 1392
Fax: 0870 444 1427
Email: docpinfo@napit.org.uk
Web: www.napit.org.uk

(5) NICEIC Certification Services Ltd
Warwick House
Houghton Hall Park, Houghton Regis, Dunstable
Bedfordshire LU5 5ZX
Tel: 0800 013 0900
Email: enquiries@dis.niceic.org.uk
Web: www.niceic.org.uk/partp/partpindex.html

Part B Defined Competence Schemes

For an enterprise the scope of whose work is limited to the design, installation, inspection and testing of defined electrical installation work, intended to operate at low or extra-low voltage, that is associated with dwellings and is undertaken in connection with, and ancillary to, some other non-electrical work.

(1) CORGI Services Ltd
CORGI (The Council for Registered Gas Installers)
1 Elmwood, Chineham Park
Crockford Lane, Basingstoke
Hants RG24 8WG
Tel: 01256 372200
Email: enquiries@corgi-gas.com
Web: www.corgi-gas-safety.com

(2) ELECSA Ltd
44 – 48 Borough High Street,
London SE1 1XB
Tel: +44 (0) 870 749 0080
Fax: +44 (0) 870 749 0085
Email: enquiries@elecsa.org.uk
Web: www.elecsa.org.uk

(3) Napit Certification Services Ltd
The Gardners Lodge,
Pleasely Vale Business Park, Mansfield,
Nottinghamshire NG19 8RL
Tel: 0870 444 1392
Fax: 0870 444 1427
Email: docpinfo@napit.org.uk
Web: www.napit.org.uk

(4) NICEIC Certification Services Ltd
Warwick House
Houghton Hall Park,
Houghton Regis, Dunstable
Bedfordshire LU5 5ZX
Tel: 0800 013 0900
Email: enquiries@dis.niceic.org.uk
Web: www.niceic.org.uk/partp/partpindex.html

(5) Oil Firing Technical Association for the Petroleum Industry Ltd (OFTEC)
OFTEC, Foxwood House,
Dobbs Lane, Kesgrave,
Ipswich IP5 2QQ
Tel: 0845 658 5080
Fax: 0845 658 5181
Email: enquiries@oftec.org
Web: www.oftec.co.uk

Management of a Defined Competence Scheme

Office of the Deputy Prime Minister criteria for management of a competent persons scheme under the Building Regulations.

The expectation is that all criteria listed below need to be demonstrated but the weight attached to each would depend on the particular circumstances in the sector concerned and the requirements on that sector in the Building Regulations.

- Financial probity and a proven track record in the field.
- Demonstrable understanding of what is involved in managing a scheme of this type and the administrative systems to do so.
- Sufficient knowledge of the Building Regulations by both scheme organisers and scheme members.
- Absence of, or methods for avoiding, conflicts of interest between the commercial interests of sponsoring or member organisations and management of the scheme.
- Minimum standard of technical competence, independently assessed where practicable, for all prospective members of a scheme. Such standards will vary from sector to sector and may be based on formal qualifications, and/or experience, taking account of any British or European standards.
- Effective means of vetting prospective members against the minimum standard.
- Commitment to allow the ODPM to monitor the scheme periodically to ensure that it delivers compliance with the Building Regulations and operates within the published rules of the scheme.
- Robust procedures in place to deal with complaints from members and disputes between members and customers.
- A rigorous system of monitoring members' compliance with the Building Regulations.
- Effective sanctions in place for dealing with non-compliance by members of the scheme.
- A system for ensuring that members issue certificates to consumers.
- If information on work completed under the scheme is to be sent to local authorities, appropriate methods to ensure rapid transfer of the information.

- Adequate consumer protection through an insurance-backed warranty, professional indemnity insurance or bond.
- Commitment to publicising the scheme and its rules as widely as possible, including the names of members of the scheme.
- Commitment to allow the ODPM to monitor the scheme periodically to ensure that it delivers compliance with the Building Regulations and is following the scheme rules.

Minimum standard of technical competence for Part P schemes

In order to help those thinking of applying to run a competent person scheme for Part P (electrical safety in dwellings) the following further guidance may be useful.

Applications should address the following on the general minimum standard of technical competence:

- How the scheme aims to ensure that electrical work in dwellings is designed, installed, inspected and tested to the standard required by BS 7671.
- How potential members of competent person schemes are to be assessed to be able to work to the standards in BS 7671.
- Assessment should be carried out as required in the Electrotechnical Assessment Scheme (EAS) (see www.iee.org/Publish/WireRegs/EAS.cfm), or an equivalent scheme, by a body accredited to certify that potential members have attained the minimum technical standard under the EAS or equivalent scheme; and
- Certifying bodies should be accredited by UKAS (or equivalent recognised accreditation body) to EN 45011. Where a certifying body does not hold such accreditation, it would need to demonstrate that it could guarantee an equivalent outcome.

Appendix F

Safety procedures

- General provisions
- Non-electrical
- Electrical
- Model form of permit-to-work

TYPICAL SAFETY INSTRUCTIONS

Part 1 – General Provisions

Scope

These Safety Instructions are for general application for work involving either, or both, non-electrical and electrical work as further described in Parts 2 and 3.

DEFINITIONS

(for use with this safety instruction).

Approved

Sanctioned in writing by the responsible director in order to satisfy in a specified manner the requirements of any or all of these Safety Instructions.

Appliance

A device requiring a supply of electricity to make it work.

Company

To be defined.

Responsible Director

The Director of the Company, partner or owner responsible for safety.

Conductor

An electrical conductor arranged to be electrically connected to a system.

Competent person

Person required to work on electrical equipment, installations and appliances and recognised by the Employer as having sufficient technical knowledge and/or experience to enable him/her to carry out the specified work properly without danger to themselves or others. It is recommended that this competence should be recognised by means of written documentation.

Customer
A person, or body, that has a contractual relationship with the Employer for the provision of goods or services.

Danger
Risk of injury to persons (and livestock where expected to be present) from:

(i) fire, electric shock and burns arising from the use of electrical energy, and
(ii) mechanical movement of electrically controlled equipment, insofar as such danger is intended to be prevented by electrical emergency switching or by electrical switching for mechanical maintenance of non-electrical parts of such equipment.

Dead
At or about zero voltage in relation to earth, and disconnected from any live system.

Earth
The conductive mass of the Earth, whose electric potential at any point is conventionally taken as zero.

Earthed
Connected to Earth through switchgear with an adequately rated earthing capacity or by approved earthing leads.

Electrical equipment
Anything used, intended to be used or installed for use to generate, provide, transmit, transform, rectify, convert, conduct, distribute, control, store, measure or use electrical energy.

Electrical installation
An assembly of associated electrical equipment supplied from a common origin to fulfil a specific purpose and having certain co-ordinated characteristics.

Isolated
The disconnection and separation of the electrical equipment from every source of electrical energy in such a way that this disconnection and separation is secure.

Live
Electrically charged.

Notices
Caution Notice – A notice in approved form conveying a warning against interference.
Danger Notice – A notice in approved form reading "Danger".

Supervisor

(i) Immediate Supervisor – a person (having adequate technical knowledge, experience and competence) who is regularly available at the location where work is in progress or who attends the work area as is necessary to ensure the safe performance and completion of work.

(ii) Personal Supervisor – a person (having adequate technical knowledge, experience and competence) such that he/she is at all times during the course of the work in the presence of the person being supervised.

Voltage

Voltage by which an installation (or part of an installation) is designated. The following ranges of nominal voltage (rms values for a.c.) are defined:

- **Extra-low.** Normally not exceeding 50 V a.c. or 120 V ripple free d.c., whether between conductors or to Earth,
- **Low.** Normally exceeding extra-low but not exceeding 1000 V a.c. or 1500 V d.c. between conductors, or 600 V a.c. or 900 V d.c. between conductors and Earth.

The actual voltage of the installation may differ from the nominal value by a quantity within normal tolerances.

- **High Voltage (HV).** A voltage exceeding 1000 V a.c. or 1500 V d.c. between conductors, or 600 V a.c. or 900 V d.c. between conductors and Earth.

Basic requirements

B1.1 Other safety rules and related procedures

In addition to the application of these Safety Instructions, other rules and procedures as issued by the Employer, or by other authorities, shall be complied with in accordance with management instructions. In that employees may be required to work in locations, or on or near electrical equipment, installations and appliances, that are not owned or controlled by the Employer, these Safety Instructions have been produced to reasonably ensure safe working, since no other rules/instructions will normally be applicable. However, where the owner has his own rules/instructions and procedures, agreement shall be reached between the Company and the owner on which rules/instructions shall be applied. Such agreement shall be made known to the employees concerned.

B1.2 Information and instruction

Arrangements shall be made to ensure:

(i) that all employees concerned are adequately informed and instructed as to any equipment, installations or appliances which are associated with work and which legal requirements, Safety Rules and related procedures shall apply; and,

(ii) that other persons who are not employees but who may be exposed to danger by the work also receive reasonably adequate information.

B1.3 Issue of Safety Instructions

Employees and other persons issued with safety instructions shall sign a receipt for a copy of these Safety Instructions (and any amendments thereto) and shall keep them in good condition and have them available for reference as necessary when work is being carried out under these Safety Instructions.

B1.4 Special procedures

Work on, or test of, equipment, installations and appliances to which rules cannot be applied, or for special reasons should not be applied, shall be carried out in accordance with recognised good practice.

B1.5 Objections

When any person receives instructions regarding work covered by these Safety Instructions and objects, on safety grounds, to the carrying out of such instructions, the person issuing them shall have the matter investigated and, if necessary, referred to a higher authority for a decision before proceeding.

B1.6 Reporting of accidents and dangerous occurrences

All accidents and dangerous occurrences, whether of an electrical nature or not, shall be reported in accordance with The Reporting of Injuries, Diseases and Dangerous Occurrences Regulations 1995.

B1.7 Health and safety

The employer and all employees have a duty to comply with the relevant provisions of the Health and Safety at Work etc. Act 1974 and with other relevant statutory provisions and the various Regulations affecting health and safety, including electrical safety. Additionally, authoritative guidance is available from the Health and Safety Executive and other sources. In addition to these statutory duties and any other responsibilities separately allocated to them, all persons who may be concerned with work as detailed in Section B1.1 shall be conversant with, and comply with, those Safety Instructions and codes of practice relevant to their duties. Ignorance of legal requirements, or of Safety Instructions and related procedures shall not be accepted as an excuse for neglect of duty. If any person has any doubt as to any of these duties he should report the matter to his immediate supervisor.

B1.8 Compliance with Safety Instructions

It is the duty of everyone who may be concerned with work covered by these Safety Instructions, to ensure their implementation and to comply with them and related codes of practice. Ignorance of the relevant legal requirements, Safety Instructions, Codes of Practice or approved procedures is not an acceptable excuse for neglect of duty. The responsibilities placed upon persons may include all or part of those detailed in this section, depending on the role of the persons. Any written authorisation given to persons to perform their designated role in implementing the Safety Instructions must indicate the work permitted. Whether employees are authorised as competent or not, all have the following duties which they must ensure are implemented:

- All employees shall comply with these Safety Instructions when carrying out work, whether instructions are issued orally or in writing.
- All employees shall use safe methods of work, safe means of access and the personal protective equipment and clothing provided for their safety.
- All employees when in receipt of work instructions shall:

  (i) be fully conversant with the nature and extent of the work to be done;
  (ii) read the contents and confirm to the person issuing the instructions that they are fully understood;
  (iii) during the course of the work, adhere to, and instruct others under their charge to adhere to, any conditions, instructions or limits specified in the work instructions;
  (iv) when in charge of work, provide immediate or personal supervision as required.

Part 2 – Non-electrical

Scope

The non-electrical part of the Safety Instructions shall be applied to work by employees in the activities that are non-electrical. This work may involve:

(i) Work on customers' premises
(ii) Work on employer's premises
(iii) Work on the public highway or in other public places.

The Safety Instructions applicable to this work are those contained in Parts 1 and 2 of the Safety Instructions. When work of an electrical nature is being carried out, all Parts (1, 2 and 3) of the Safety Instructions apply.

Basic Safety precautions

B2.1 General principle

The general principle is to avoid accidents. Most accidents arise from simple causes and can be prevented by taking care.

B2.2 Protective clothing and equipment

The wearing of protective clothing and the use of protective equipment can, in appropriate circumstances, considerably reduce the severity of injury should an accident occur. Where any work under these Safety Instructions and related procedures takes place, appropriate safety equipment and protective clothing of an approved type shall be issued and used. At all times employees are expected to wear sensible clothing and footwear having regard to the work being carried out. Further references are made, in particular circumstances, to the use of gloves. Hard hats must be worn at all times when there is a risk of head injury and particularly on building sites. Where there is danger from flying particles of metal, concrete or stone, suitable eye protection must be provided and must be used by employees. If necessary, additional screens must be provided to protect other persons in the vicinity.

B2.3 Good housekeeping
Tidiness, wherever work is carried out, is the foundation of safety; good housekeeping will help to ensure a clean, tidy and safe place of work.

Particular attention should be paid to:

(i) picking up dropped articles immediately;
(ii) wiping up any patches of oil, grease or water as soon as they appear and, if necessary, spreading sand or sawdust;
(iii) removing rubbish and scrap to the appropriate place;
(iv) preventing objects falling from a height by using containers for hand tools and other loose material;
(v) ensuring stairs and exits are kept clear.

No job is completed until all loose gear, tools and materials have been cleared away and the workplace left clean and tidy. Most falls are caused by slippery substances or loose objects on the floor and good housekeeping will remove most of the hazards that can occur.

B2.4 Safe access
It is essential that every place of work is at all times provided with safe means of access and exit, and these routes must be maintained in a safe condition. Keeping the workplace tidy minimises the risk of falling which is the major cause of accidents, but certain special hazards associated with work in confined spaces require particular attention.

B2.4.1 Ladders
All ladders should be of sound construction, uniquely identified and free from apparent defects. This is of particular importance in connection with timber ladders. The following practices should always be observed:

Ladders should be checked before use. Any defects must be reported and the equipment clearly marked and not used until repaired. All ladders should be regularly inspected by a competent person and a record kept. Ladders in use should stand on a level and firm footing. Loose packing should not be used to support the base. Ladders should be used at the correct angle, i.e., for every four metres up, the bottom of the ladder must be one metre out. Ladders should be lashed at the top when in use, but when this is not practicable they should be held secure at the bottom. The ladder top should extend to a height of at least one metre above any landing place. Hand tools and other material should not be carried in the hand when ascending or descending ladders. A bag and sash line should be used. Suitable crawling ladders or boards must be used when working on asbestos, cement and other fragile roofs. Permanent warning notices should be placed at the means of access to these roofs. (NB: In a situation where no ladder is available, and the work requires a small step up, it is the employee's responsibility to ensure that any other article used for the purpose is totally suitable.)

B2.4.2 Openings in floors

Every floor opening must be guarded, and it is important that other occupants of the workplace are made aware of these hazards. In addition to the risk of persons falling through any opening, there is also a risk from falling objects and safe placing of tools, materials and other objects when working near openings, holes or edges, or at any height, will also prevent accidents. If work has to be carried out in confined spaces such as tunnels and underground chambers, the atmosphere may be deficient in oxygen or may contain dangerous fumes or substances. The Electricity Association Engineering Recommendations, ERG64, Safety in Cableways or similar must be followed in these circumstances.

B2.5 Lighting

Good lighting, whether natural or artificial, is essential to the safety of people whether at the workplace or moving about. If natural lighting is inadequate, it must be supplemented by adequate and suitable artificial lighting. If danger may arise from a power failure, adequate emergency lighting is required.

B2.6 Lifting and handling

All employees must be trained in the appropriate lifting and handling techniques according to the type of work undertaken.

B2.7 Fire precautions

All employees must be thoroughly conversant with the procedure to be followed in the event of fire. Whether working on customers' premises or elsewhere, employees should familiarise themselves with escape routes, fire precautions, etc., before commencing work. Fire exits must always be kept clear, and access to fire fighting equipment unobstructed. All fire fighting equipment that is the Employer's responsibility must be regularly inspected, maintained and recorded whether by local supervisor, safety supervisor or appropriate third party. Individuals should report any apparent damage to equipment.

B2.8 Hand tools

Hand tools must be suitable for the purpose for which they are being used and are the responsibility of those using them. They must be maintained in good order and any which are worn or otherwise defective must be reported to a supervisor. Approved insulated tools must be available for work on live electrical equipment.

B2.9 Mechanical handling

Fork-lift and similar trucks must only be driven by operators who have been properly trained, tested and certified for the type of trucks they have to operate. Supervisors should control the issue and return of the truck keys and they should ensure that a daily check of the truck and its controls is carried out by the operator.

B2.10 Portable power tools

All portable electrical apparatus including cables, portable transformers and other ancillary equipment should be inspected before use and maintained and tested at regular intervals.

Trailing cables are frequently damaged and exposed to wet conditions. Users must report all such damage and other defects as soon as possible, and the faulty equipment must be immediately withdrawn from use. When not in use power tools should be switched off and disconnected from the source of supply.

B2.11 Welding, burning and heating processes

B2.11.1 General

Welding, burning and heating processes involving the use of gas and electricity demand a high degree of skill and detailed knowledge of the appropriate safety requirements. Specific safety instructions will be issued to employees using such equipment. Suitable precautions should be taken, particularly when working overhead, to prevent fire or other injury from falling or flying sparks. All heating, burning and welding equipment must be regularly inspected, and a record kept.

B2.11.2 Propane

Propane is a liquefied petroleum gas stored under pressure in cylinders which must be stored vertically in cool, well-ventilated areas, away from combustible material, heat sources and corrosive conditions. Cylinders must be handled carefully and not allowed to fall from a height; when transported, they must always be carried in an approved restraint. When the cylinder valve is opened the liquid boils, giving off a highly flammable gas. The gas is heavier than air and can give rise to a highly explosive mixture. It is essential, therefore, that valves are turned off after use.

B2.12 Machinery

All machinery shall be guarded as necessary to prevent mechanical hazards. Facilities shall be provided for isolating and locking off the power to machinery. Work on machines shall not commence unless isolation and locking off from all sources of power has been effected and permits to work issued.

Part 3 – Electrical

Scope

This part of the Safety Instructions shall be applied to electrical work. This work may involve:

(i) Work on employers' equipment;
(ii) Work on customers' electrical installations;
(iii) Work on customers' electrical appliances.

This work will normally be concerned with equipment, installations and appliances at low voltages. In the event of work needing to be carried out on high voltage equipment and installations (i.e. where the voltage exceeds 1000 volts a.c.), additional instructions and procedures laid down for High Voltage work must be issued to those employees who carry out this work.

Basic safety precautions

B3.1 General principle

As a general principle, and wherever reasonably practicable, work should only be carried out on equipment that is dead and isolated from all sources of supply. Such equipment should be proved dead by means of an approved voltage testing device which should be tested before and after verification, or by clear evidence of isolation taking account of the possibility of wrong identification or circuit labelling. Equipment should always be assumed to be live until it is proved dead. This is particularly important where there is a possibility of backfeed from another source of supply.

B3.2 Information prior to commencement of work

According to the complexity of the installation, the following information may need to be provided before specified work is carried out:

(i) details of the supply to the premises, and to the system and equipment on which work is to be carried out;
(ii) details of the relevant circuits and equipment and the means of isolation;
(iii) details of any customer's safety rules or procedures that may be applicable to the work;
(iv) the nature of any processes or substances which could give rise to a hazard associated with the work, or other special conditions that could affect the working area, such as the need for special access arrangements;
(v) emergency arrangements on site;
(vi) the name and designation of the person nominated to ensure effective liaison during the course of the work.

Where the available information, or the action to be taken as a result of it, is considered by the person in charge of the work to be inadequate for safe working, such work should not proceed until that inadequacy has been removed or a decision obtained from a person in higher authority. Defects affecting safe working should be reported to the appropriate supervisor.

B3.3 Precautions to be taken before work commences on dead electrical equipment

In addition to any special precautions to be taken at the site of the work, such as for the presence of hazardous processes or substances, the following electrical precautions should be taken, according to the circumstances, before work commences on dead electrical equipment:

(i) the electrical equipment should first be properly identified and disconnected from all points of supply by the opening of circuit-breakers, isolating switches, the removal of fuses, links or current-limiting devices, or other suitable means. Approved Notices, warning against interference, should be affixed at all points of disconnection.
(ii) all reasonably practicable steps should be taken to prevent the electrical equipment being made live inadvertently. This may be achieved, according to the circumstances, by taking one or more of the following precautions:

(a) approved locks should be used to lock off all switches etc. at points where the electrical equipment and associated circuits can be made live. This should be additional to any lock applied by any other party; the keys to all locks should be retained by the person in charge of the work or in a specially provided key safe,
(b) any fuses, links or current-limiting devices involved in the isolation procedures should be retained in the possession of the person in charge of the work, and
(c) in the case of portable apparatus, where isolation has been by removal of a plug from a socket-outlet, suitable arrangements should be made to prevent unauthorised re-connection,
(d) approved notices should be placed at points where the electrical equipment and associated circuits can be made live.

(iii) the electrical equipment should be proved dead by the proper use of an approved voltage testing device and/or by clear evidence of isolation, such as physically tracing a circuit. Approved testing devices should be checked immediately before and after use to ensure that they are in working order,
(iv) when work is carried out on timeswitched or other automatically controlled equipment or circuits, the fuses or other means of isolation controlling such equipment or circuits should be removed. On no account should reliance be placed on the timeswitches, limit switches, lock-out push buttons etc., or on any other auxiliary equipment, as means of isolation,
(v) where necessary, approved notices should be displayed to indicate any exposed live conductors in the working zone,
(vi) when it is required to work on dead equipment situated in a substation or similar place where there are exposed live conductors, or adjacent to High Voltage plant, the safe working area should be defined by a person authorised in writing under the Safety Rules or under procedures controlling that plant, and all subsequent work must be conducted in accordance with such rules or procedures. Where necessary, the exposed live conductors should be adequately screened in an approved manner or by other approved means taken to avoid danger from the live conductors.

B3.4 Precautions to be taken before work commences on or near live equipment
No person shall be engaged in any work activity on or so near any live conductor (other than one suitably covered with insulating material so as to prevent danger) that danger may arise unless:

(i) it is unreasonable in all the circumstances for it to be dead; and
(ii) it is reasonable in all the circumstances for them to be at work on or near it while it is live; and
(iii) suitable precautions (including where necessary the provision of suitable protective equipment) are taken to prevent injury (Regulation 14, Electricity at Work Regulations). Where work is to be carried out on live equipment the following protective equipment should be provided, maintained and used, by adequately trained personnel, in accordance with the Safety Rules or local procedures as appropriate:

(a) approved screens or screening material,
(b) approved insulating stands in the form of hardwood gratings or approved rubber insulating mats,
(c) approved insulated tools, and
(d) approved insulating gloves.

When testing, including functional testing or adjustment of electrical equipment requires covers to be removed so that terminals or connections that are live, or can be made live, are exposed, precautions should be taken to prevent unauthorised approach to or interference with live parts. This may be achieved by keeping the work area under the immediate surveillance of an employee or by erecting a suitable barrier, with Approved Notices displayed warning against approach and interference. When live terminals or site barriers are being adjusted, only approved insulated tools should be used. Additional precautions may be required because of the nature of any hazardous process or special circumstances present at the site of the work. Work on live equipment should only be undertaken where it is unreasonable in all the circumstances for it to be made dead.

B3.5 Operation of switchgear

The operation of switchgear should only be carried out by a Competent Person after he/she has obtained full knowledge and details of the installation and the effects of the intended switching operations. Under no circumstances must equipment be made operable by hand signals or by a pre-arranged time interval.

Fig B3.1: Model form of permit-to-work

MODEL FORM OF PERMIT-TO-WORK (FRONT)

PERMIT-TO-WORK

1. ISSUE No...............................

To...

The following apparatus has been made safe in accordance with the Safety Rules for the work detailed on this Permit to-Work to proceed:

....

....

....

TREAT ALL OTHER APPARATUS AS LIVE

Circuit Main Earths are applied at

....

....

Other precautions and information and any local instructions applicable to the work, notes 1 and 2.

....

....

....

The following work is to be carried out: ....

....

....

....

Name (Block capitals)...

Signature...

Time... Date..

MODEL FORM OF PERMIT-TO-WORK (BACK)

2. RECEIPT

(note 2)

I accept responsibility for carrying out the work on the Apparatus detailed on this Permit-to-Work and no attempt will be made by me, or by the persons under my charge, to work on any other Apparatus.

Name (Block capitals)..

Signature..

Time.. Date..

3. CLEARANCE

(note 3)

All persons under my charge have been withdrawn and warned that it is no longer safe to work on the Apparatus detailed on this Permit-to-Work, and all Additional Earths have been removed.

The work is complete*/incomplete*
All gear and tools have*/have not* been removed

Name (Block capitals)..

Signature..

Time..Date..

*Delete words not applicable

....

....

4. CANCELLATION

(note 3)

This Permit-to-Work is cancelled.
Name (Block capitals)..

Signature..

Time..Date..

5. Diagram

The diagram should show:

(a) the safe zone where work is to be carried out
(b) the points of isolation
(c) the places where earths have been applied, and
(d) the locations where 'danger' notices have been posted.

Notes on Model Form of Permit-to-Work

1. ACCESS TO AND WORK IN FIRE PROTECTED AREAS

Automatic control

Unless alternative Approved procedures apply because of special circumstances then before access to, or work or other activities are carried out in, any enclosure protected by automatic fire extinguishing equipment:

(a) The automatic control shall be rendered inoperative and the equipment left on hand control. A Caution Notice shall be attached.

(b) Precautions taken to render the automatic control inoperative and the conditions under which it may be restored shall be noted on any Safety Document or written instruction issued for access, work or other activity in the protected enclosure.

(c) The automatic control shall be restored immediately after the persons engaged on the work or other activity have withdrawn from the protected enclosure.

2. PROCEDURE FOR ISSUE AND RECEIPT

(a) A Permit-to-Work shall be explained and issued to the person in direct charge of the work, who after reading its contents to the person issuing it, and confirming that he understands it and is conversant with the nature and extent of the work to be done, shall sign its receipt and its duplicate.

(b) The recipient of a Permit-to-Work shall be a Competent Person who shall retain the Permit-to-Work in his possession at all times whilst work is being carried out.

(c) Where more than one Working Party is involved a Permit-to-Work shall be issued to the Competent Person in direct charge of each Working Party and these shall, where necessary, be cross-referenced one with another.

3. PROCEDURE FOR CLEARANCE AND CANCELLATION

(a) A Permit-to-Work shall be cleared and cancelled:

  (i) when work on the Apparatus or Conductor for which it was issued has been completed;

  (ii) when it is necessary to change the person in charge of the work detailed on the Permit-to-Work;

  (iii) at the discretion of the Responsible Person when it is necessary to interrupt or suspend the work detailed on the Permit-to-Work.

(b) The recipient shall sign the clearance and return to the Responsible Person who shall cancel it. In all cases the recipient shall indicate in the clearance section whether the work is "complete" or "incomplete" and that all gear and tools "have" or "have not" been removed.

(c) Where more than one Permit-to-Work has been issued for work on Apparatus or Conductors associated with the same Circuit Main Earths, the Controlling Engineer shall ensure that all such Permits-to-Work have been cancelled before the Circuit Main Earths are removed.

4. PROCEDURE FOR TEMPORARY WITHDRAWAL OR SUSPENSION

Where there is a requirement for a Permit-to-Work to be temporarily withdrawn or suspended this shall be in accordance with an Approved procedure.

Index

Index

IEE Wiring Regulations and associated publications

The IEE prepares regulations for the safety of electrical installations for buildings, the IEE Wiring Regulations (BS 7671: Requirements for Electrical Installations) which have now become the standard for the UK and many other countries. It also recommends, internationally, the requirements for ships and offshore installations. The IEE provides guidance on the application of the installation regulations through publications focused on the various activities from design of the installation through to final test and then maintenance. This includes a series of seven guidance notes, two codes of practice, a CD-ROM, and model forms for use in wiring installations.

Requirements for Electrical Installations BS 7671: 2001 (IEE Wiring Regulations, 16th Edition including Amendments 1& 2: 2004)
Order book WR250 Paperback 2001
ISBN: 0-86341-373-0 **£49**
Order book WR251Loose-leaf 2001
ISBN: 0-86341-375-7 **£49**

On-Site Guide (BS 7671: 2001 16th Edition Wiring Regulations including Amendments, 1 & 2: 2004)
Order book WR241 180pp Paperback 2001
ISBN: 0-86341-374-9 **£17**

BS 7671: 2001 on CD-ROM, 6th Edition
Order CD WR861 CD-ROM single workstation version 2004
ISBN: 0-86341-464-8 **£395**
Order CD WR862 CD-ROM Network version (10 concurrent users)
ISBN: 0-86341-465-6 **£1200**

Wiring Matters Magazine **Free**
If you wish to receive a FREE copy or advertise in Wiring Matters please contact: advertising@iee.org.uk

IEE Guidance Notes

A series of Guidance Notes has been issued, each of which enlarges upon and amplifies the particular requirements of a part of the 16th Edition Wiring Regulations.

Guidance Note 1: Selection and Erection of Equipment, 4th Edition
Order book WR234 232pp Paperback 2002
ISBN: 0-85296-989-9 **£30**

Guidance Note 2: Isolation and Switching, 4th Edition
Order book WR235 69pp Paperback 2003
ISBN: 0-85296-990-2 **£17**

Guidance Note 3: Inspection and Testing, 4th Edition
Order book WR236 120pp Paperback 2002
ISBN: 0-85296-991-0 **£20**

Guidance Note 4: Protection Against Fire, 4th Edition
Order book WR237 85pp Paperback 2003
ISBN: 0-85296-992-9 **£17**

Guidance Note 5: Protection Against Electric Shock, 4th Edition
Order book WR238 85pp Paperback 2003
ISBN: 0-85296-993-7 **£20**

Continued overleaf ►

Guidance Note 6: Protection Against Overcurrent, 4th Edition
Order book WR239 103pp Paperback 2003
ISBN: 0-85296-994-5 **£20**

Guidance Note 7: Special Locations, 2nd Edition
Order book WR240 100pp Paperback 2003
ISBN: 0-85296-995-3 **£25**

Commentary on IEE Wiring Regulations (16th Edition BS 7671: 2001)
Order book NS031 438pp Hardback 2002
ISBN: 0-85296-237-1 **£45**

Electrical Maintenance
Order book WR229 165pp Paperback 1999
ISBN: 0-85296-769-1 **£35**

Regulations for the Electrical and Electronic Equipment of Ships with Recommended Practice for their Implementation
c. 100 pages Paperback
To be published 2005 **£45**

Recommendations for the Electrical and Electronic Equipment of Mobile and Fixed Offshore Installations
Order book WR401 212pp Paperback 1992
ISBN 0-85296-528-1 **£60**
Ist Amendment only 1995
ISBN 0-85296-846-9 **£10**

Electrical Craft Principles, Volumes 1 & 2, 4th Edition
Order book ST101 318pp
Volume 1 Paperback 1995
ISBN: 0-85296-811-6 **£18**
Order book ST102 409pp
Volume 2 Paperback 1995
ISBN: 0-85296-833-7 **£18**

Code of Practice for In-Service Inspection and Testing of Electrical Equipment
Order book WR233 Paperback 81pp 2001
ISBN: 0-85296-776-4 **£30**

Model Forms

The IEE, jointly with the Institution of Mechanical Engineers IMechE, issues the following Model Forms, and guidance.

MF/1 (Revision 4)
Order book PA101 2000 Edition
ISBN: 0-85296-759-4 **£50**

MF/2 (Revision 1)
Order book TR009, 1999 Edition
ISBN: 0-85296-858-2 **£50**

MF 3 (Revision 1)
Order book PA104 2001 Edition
ISBN: 0-85296-202-9 **£27**

Commentary on MF/1
Order book PA103 2001 Edition 2001
ISBN: 0-85296-007-7 **£35**

Commentary on MF/2
Order book PA102 2000 Edition
ISBN: 0-85296-758-6 **£39**

Commentary on MF/4
Order book PA401 2003 Edition
ISBN: 0-86341-369-2 **£15**

Keep up to date with technical issues with the IEE www.iee.org/technical

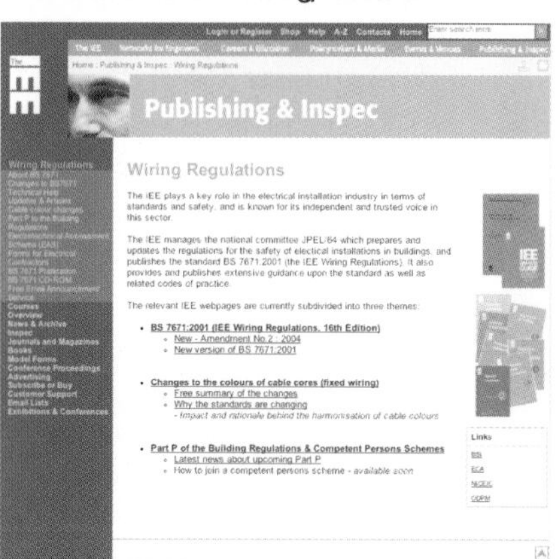

For more information, visit www.iee.org/wiringregs

Publications Order Form

Photocopies of this order form are acceptable.

Payment Methods

1. By cheque made payable to IEE
2. By credit/debit card

☐ Visa ☐ Mastercard ☐ American Express

☐ Switch Issue No_____

No: ☐☐☐☐ ☐☐☐☐ ☐☐☐☐ ☐☐☐☐

Expiry date: ____________________

Signature: ____________________

(Orders not valid unless signed)

Cardholder name: ____________________

Cardholder address: ____________________

Country: ____________________

3. By official company purchase order (please attach copy)

EU VAT number: ____________________

How to Order

1. By phone: +44(0)1438 767328

2. By fax +44(0)1438 742792

3. By email: sales@iee.org

4. By post: IEE, PO Box 96, Stevenage, SG1 2SD

Name: ____________________

Job Title: ____________________

Company/Institution: ____________________

Address: ____________________

Country: ____________________

Tel: __________ Fax: __________

Email: ____________________

ORDERING INFORMATION

Quantity	Book No.	Title/Author	Price (£)
	WR/		
	WR/		
	WR/		
	WR/		
	WR/		
	WR/		
	WR/		
	WR/		
	WR/		
	WR/		
	WR/		
	WR/		
	WR/		

* Postage/Handling: Please add £1.50/item for handling unless order is prepaid. Postage is free within the UK. Outside UK, add 10% (Europe) and 15% (Rest of World) of total order value for accelerated surface post. Airmail and courier rates are available on request.

The IEE is a not-for-profit organisation, registered as a charity in the UK.

Subtotal __________
+ Postage/Handling* __________
+ VAT if applicable __________
TOTAL __________

This form to be sent to:
The IEE, Publishing Sales, PO Box 96, Stevenage, SG1 2SD

Membership of the IEE

Passionate about engineering? Committed to your career?

Do you want to join an organisation that is inspiring, insightful and innovative?

The IEE is an international organisation for electronics, electrical, manufacturing and IT professionals, with specifically tailored products, services and qualifications to meet the needs of today's technology industry.

You could take advantage of...

- Significant discounts for all IEE events
- Comprehensive professional support, including mentoring, career guidance, CV creation and privileged access to job opportunities in the UK and Overseas
- Your regular copy of the award-winning IEE Review PLUS your choice of specialist engineering magazine – plus 20% off all other IEE publications
- Privileged access to the world's leading technical library with 75,000 books and 5,000 journals
- Recognised industry qualifications (CEng, IEng and EngTech)
- A whole host of additional exciting products and services.

Join online today www.iee.org/membership
For further information tel: +44 (0)1438 767282 or email membership@iee.org

Professional Registration

What type of registration is for you?

Chartered Engineers (CEng) are characterised by their ability to develop appropriate solutions to engineering problems, using new or existing technologies, through innovation, creativity and change. They might develop and apply new technologies, promote advanced designs and design methods, introduce new and more efficient production techniques, marketing and construction concepts, pioneer new engineering services and management methods. Chartered Engineers are variously engaged in technical and commercial leadership and possess interpersonal skills.

Incorporated Engineers (IEng) are characterised by their ability to act as exponents of today's technology through creativity and innovation. To this end, they maintain and manage applications of current and developing technology, and may undertake engineering design, development, manufacture, construction and operation. Incorporated Engineers are variously engaged in technical and commercial management and possess effective interpersonal skills.

Engineering Technicians (EngTech) are involved in applying proven techniques and procedures to the solution of practical engineering problems. They carry supervisory or technical responsibility, and are competent to exercise creative aptitudes and skills within defined fields of technology. Professional Engineering Technicians contribute to the design, development, manufacture, commissioning, operation or maintenance of products, equipment, processes or services. Professional Engineering Technicians are required to apply safe systems of work.

For further information on Professional Registration (CEng/IEng/EngTech) contact +44 (0)1438 767282 or email membership@iee.org

Membership Application Form

SECTION A: Personal Information

Title________ Surname ________________

First Name(s) ________________

Date of Birth: Day ____ Month ____ Year ____

Address ________________

____

____________ Postcode ________

Mobile: ________________

Email: ________________

SECTION B: Engineering Magazines

On admission you will receive one of the magazines listed below free of charge. Please indicate which magazine you wish to receive by ticking one box only

- ☐ Communications Engineer
- ☐ Computing & Control Engineering
- ☐ Electronics Systems & Software
- ☐ Engineering Management
- ☐ Manufacturing Engineer
- ☐ Power Engineer
- ☐ Information Professional

SECTION C: Education

Please provide details of all qualifications obtained and any that are currently being undertaken e.g. Advanced Modern Apprenticeship, ONC, NVQ 3, HND, BSc, BEng etc

Type of Qualification ____________ Title of Course ____________

Name of Educational Establishment ________________

Mode of Study FT ☐ PT ☐ SW ☐ Period of Study: From ______ To ______

SECTION D: Obligation and Certificate

I confirm that the statements made on this form are to the best of my knowledge true. I agree to comply with the Charter and Bylaws of the IEE and whilst remaining a member I will do my best to promote the interests of the IEE.

I understand that the information provided on this form will be processed by the IEE for its sole use and that of its subsidiary companies for the purpose of providing goods and services ordered by you and for billing, accounts and sending you information about IEE services and offers.

Signature of Applicant ________________ Date ________

SECTION E: How to Pay **(Alternatively please call the credit card hotline 01438 765 607)**

Age at 1 January	Subscription Rates	
35 and over	£92.00	☐
29 - 34	£76.00	☐
26 - 28	£51.00	☐
21 - 25	£36.00	☐
Student (Full time/Part time)	£12.00	☐

(Please tick box)

Charge Card Authority:

Card number: ☐☐☐☐ ☐☐☐☐ ☐☐☐☐ ☐☐☐☐

Valid from: ☐☐ ☐☐ Expiry date: ☐☐ ☐☐

Issue number: ☐☐

Name on credit card ________________

Address ________________

____

____________ Postcode ________

For office use only: Membership Number ☐☐☐☐☐☐☐☐

To the IEE: I authorise you until further notice in writing to charge my Visa/MasterCard account unspecified amounts in respect of payments to the IEE as and when they become due

Signature ________________ Date ________

This form to be sent to:
The IEE, Membership Admissions, PO Box 96, Stevenage, SG1 2SD

ET/WR04